THE WRITING ON THE WALL

TERENCE COPLEY

Religious and Moral Education Press
An imprint of Chansitor Publications Ltd,
a wholly owned subsidiary of Hymns Ancient & Modern Ltd
St Mary's Works, St Mary's Plain
Norwich, Norfolk NR3 3BH

First published 1994

ISBN 1 85175-019-3

ACKNOWLEDGEMENTS

Once again Mary Mears of the publishers, RMEP, has proved an
enthusiastic and very capable accessory, with a natural talent for crime,
and for her constructive and criminal editorial support, real thanks.
Youngsters have trialled this book in whole or part and made suggestions
to improve the plot. I owe some ideas to them, including once again that
Devon sleuth Claire C.

I have been helped to get something of the many kosher flavours of
Judaism from the writings of Leo Baeck, Lionel Blue, Douglas Charing,
Ben Eliezer, Isidore Epstein, Elizabeth Koltun, Jonathan Magonet, Leo
Trepp and Angela Wood. Frank Gent's local contribution of humour and
encouragement from a 'smorthodox' point of view and his wider referral
for consultation of some of the material have been much appreciated.

Exeter University student teachers have urged me to get on with more
crimes in this world-faiths series and so it may be that the Quicksolve
Detective Agency will rise again!

Note
Information on how this book can be used in schools is provided on
pages 109 to 110.

Designed and typeset by Topics Visual Information, Exeter

Illustrations by Clive Wakfer

Printed in Great Britain by BPC Wheatons Ltd, Exeter, for Chansitor
Publications Ltd, Norwich

About You

In this book, you, the reader, play the role of one of the partners in the Quicksolve Detective Agency.

The Quicksolve team are thrilled with their earlier success in the case of *Sudden Death at the Vicarage*. Imagine you are just tucking into a celebration meal when you are interrupted by a phone call. A local synagogue has rung Quicksolve and asked them to investigate a new and baffling mystery. Your boss puts you in charge of the case – starting at once!

Before you go to the synagogue you call in at the Quicksolve office to see if they have more information.

1

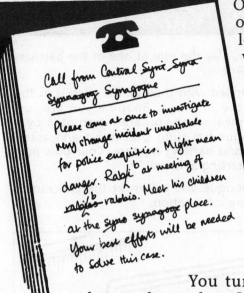

Call from Central Synr Synr Synagog Synagogue

Please come at once to investigate very strange incident unsuitable for police enquiries. Might mean danger. Rabi⁰ at meeting of rabbis⁰ rabbis. Meet his children at the Synr synagoge place. Your best efforts will be needed to solve this case.

On your desk, next to an open dictionary, is a longer phone message, written for you by your assistant while you were out at your ill fated lunch. It looks like your assistant's best spelling only just made it! If you want to check the difference between 'rabbis' and 'rabies', you may need to use the open dictionary on your desk.

You turn over in your mind what you know about Jews already:

- They don't eat pork.
- They've got a holy day they're not supposed to work on.
- During the Second World War many of them were killed.
- Their religious leaders are called rabbis.
- Their Bible is what Christians call the Old Testament.
- Moses was one of their most famous leaders.

You think you can also remember that synagogues are their places of worship. It isn't much to start you off on a Jewish case. So you leave a message asking your assistant to start finding information about the Jewish religion from encyclopedias and by going to the local library to see what books they've got. It might help later.

You check where the Central Synagogue (or synogoge!) is on the map and decide to drive down there straight away.

2

How You Play Detective

In this investigation you will need to work out:

- who committed the crime,
- who was the intended victim,
- the motive or reason for the crime.

If you can find all three correctly, you will have solved the case.

Every few pages in this book, you are asked to choose what you, the detective, do next. When you have decided which clue to follow up or what action to take, you go to another page and read on. But, as in real-life detection, you are working against time. There are several ways of reaching the correct solution to the case, but some take longer than others. Sometimes you will have to decide whether to spend time on extra clues, or whether to manage without. Some choices take longer and tell you in advance that you will have to 'add 1 hour to your time score'. When you turn to some other pages, you may find that a choice you have made loses you an hour when you weren't expecting it to. This too is like real life because some things take longer than we expect – but the hour must be added to your time score. It is important to write down all these extra hours so that you can keep track of your time score. They are not real hours that you have to add on to reach the solution!

Your time score starts at zero at the beginning of the case. At the very end of the book you will work out a final score based on how much of the solution you got right as well as how long it took you, i.e. the size of your time score. If you use extra clues that add to your time spent, you may be much more likely to get the right solution. If you don't use them, you will be going for a quicker solution, but your chances of getting it wrong may be much higher. It's up to you to weigh up the risks!

You will need a pen or pencil and paper for keeping a note of your time score. It might be useful to have a pad handy to jot down names of suspects, or details of the crime. As you near the end of the book, you may want to write down your deductions – or guesses – about the solution before you actually go on to check it. It's also ὲ good idea to have something you can use as a bookmark so that you don't lose your place, especially if you have to jump to another page to read a clue then back again to where you came from.

Now read on. Good luck with the case! Quicksolve are relying on you.

You arrive at the synagogue

The synagogue is a large square building, two storeys tall, built of brick, with a small notice-board by the double doors at the entrance. Two youngsters are standing on the pavement outside, obviously waiting for you to arrive. They run up to the car as you get out.

'Excuse me, are you from Quicksolve?' They look with interest as you produce your identity card.

'So you're a real private detective?' says the girl.

'Solved any murder cases?' the boy asks. Before you can answer, they introduce themselves as Rachel and Simon Levy, explaining that they are the rabbi's children but that their dad has been called away. He has left them to meet you and show you round the synagogue, the scene of the crime, as they keep calling it. Rachel is tall and dark haired with blue eyes, very fashionably dressed. She looks about thirteen. Her brother looks a year or so older but he is not so tall and he is rather wider! He has a small round embroidered sort of cap on top of his head.

Rachel has the key to the door. As she unlocks it your professional eye notes that the door has a complicated mortice lock, not easy for any key to open. She leads the way in. Passing through an entrance porch full of notices and coat pegs, then through two more double doors, you find yourself in a large hall. There is a raised platform in the middle of the ground floor with railings round it and a sort of desk inside. You can see another platform and a pair of long crimson curtains at the far end. A gallery runs round the top on three sides, the platform end facing you being left clear.

You wonder if there are any rules about what you can and can't wear in synagogues, as you don't want to offend anyone by being unsuitably dressed.

4

'Boys and men – and married women – must cover their heads,' Simon explains, touching his own head-covering cap. Although it is empty, you can sense that this building is a very special place for Rachel and Simon.

5

'Well, what do you make of it?' asks Rachel.

'You can see why it doesn't seem like a case for the police,' adds Simon. You look around. Actually you can't see any sign of disturbance. No breaking and entering. No obvious damage. No robbery. No blood. No corpse! You  gaze at the windows. Patterns and Jewish symbols appear in them. You recognize the Star of David because you've seen it on the flag of Israel.

At the front is what looks like a giant candlestick. You guess it must stand for something, a sort of mega-badge, because there aren't any candles in it.

But nothing looks out of place. Above the long curtains on the platform at the other end is some sort of writing, with a different alphabet. Books lie tidily on the ledges in front of each of the seats around where you are standing. You assume they are for use in the services. Everything seems to be in order. It's far from obvious, even to your detective eye, that any crime has been committed.

'Well,' says Rachel, to your slight dismay, 'what do you make of it?'

'Err, I'm not honestly sure what the "it" is,' you venture, deciding to be honest. 'Has the collection money been stolen?'

'Oh, of course, I'm sorry. It looks so obvious to us, because we're in here so often that we noticed it straight away. It's nothing to do with the collection. Actually, we don't have collections of money during the services like some Christian churches do. We have an annual subscription instead.'

'You mean people are charged a membership fee?'

'Yes, but if you can't afford it you don't get thrown out!'

6

'So there's no money here?'

'Oh, no! This has got nothing to do with money. Look over here,' says Simon, pointing to the wall. There, on the right-hand side wall, you see an inscription, in the same sort of letters as the writing over the curtains on the platform.

'There!' says Simon, triumphantly, looking to you for some sort of comment.

'I'm sorry,' you say, slightly hesitantly, 'I don't see what's wrong.'

'That's what's wrong,' says Rachel, pointing to the writing. 'We didn't write it, that's what!' But it has been so carefully stencilled or painted onto the wall that it looks as if it's meant to be there.

'So it's not a synagogue inscription or text, then, like the one over those curtains?' you say, looking towards the front again.

'Simon, we're both being stupid assuming that at Quicksolve they'll know all about Jews and Jewish customs just because they're detectives. We need to do a bit of explaining,' says Rachel. 'If you like,' she goes on, trying to keep in on the detective act, 'we could come with you on the case, as it's school holidays at the moment. Then we could help you on the Jewish background.'

'Yes,' agrees Simon enthusiastically, 'and if we get stuck we can ask Mum or Dad anything you want to know about Judaism.' You're grateful for the offer. Insider knowledge will help you to understand what you're looking at.

First, Rachel and Simon explain to you that behind the curtains on the front platform are the doors to the Aron Kodesh, or Holy Ark. 'Aron' is the Hebrew word for box or cabinet. Inside the synagogue Ark are the precious handwritten scrolls of the Jewish Torah, the first five books of the Jewish and Christian Bibles. The Torah is the basis of Jewish beliefs and how Jews try to live. Above those doors are the opening words of each of the Ten Commandments. The language is Hebrew, the language of the Jewish Bible and of modern Israel. But the youngsters tell you that the writing on the wall beside you is different. It has not been produced by and for synagogue members. It just appeared. An unknown person did it.

'But it doesn't look like graffiti,' you point out. 'It isn't spray paint. It looks more like something done by a professional sign-writer. I thought it was similar to the writing over the Ark doors. Is it Hebrew writing? When did it appear?'

'Last night,' explains Simon. 'That's the mystery. When the synagogue was locked for the night, it wasn't there, and when it was unlocked this morning, there it was! And not a thing touched or moved, not a door forced open. No clue at all. But it is in Hebrew letters like the writing over the Ark doors.'

'Did your dad call the police?' you ask.

8

'No,' says Rachel, 'after all, there's been no break-in and nothing's been taken. Even the writing's been done so that it looks as if it belongs here. You mistook it for part of the furniture.'

'But how was it done – and why?'

'That's what Dad wants you to find out. He says the police will be much too busy to bother with this, but it's shaken him.'

'How do you mean?'

'Well, I don't think he likes the idea that someone could have come in, using a key or a duplicate key, and done this. If they've come once, they could come again and you don't know what they'll get up to next time....' You suddenly become aware of the silence of the place, the galleries above you with their bench seats, the echo of Rachel and Simon's voices in the empty building. Someone might just be behind one of those upstairs seats listening even now.... It's creepy.

You start to wonder what's going on. Is this some sort of joke? Is it a surprise for someone? Is it a message? Has someone done this to get at the Jews who worship here? You know that for thousands of years Jews have been attacked, even killed, simply for being Jewish, being different.

You have three choices:

- You can go back to the Quicksolve office to find out about attacks on Jews, in case that's behind this writing, and to contact the local newspaper office, to see if any attacks have occurred in this area recently. If you choose to do this, it will take time and you will have to **add 1 hour to your time score**. If you still want to do this, go to page 11.

- You can stay here and find out more about the writing from Rachel and Simon. If you want to do this, go to page 14.

- You can go to the Levys' house and wait for Rachel and Simon's dad, David Levy, the rabbi, to get home. If you want to do this, go to page 10.

9

You go to the Levys' house

The rabbi doesn't come home, because he's delayed at a long meeting. You wait for an hour without success, losing time you weren't expecting to lose.

Add 1 hour to your time score.

You now have three choices:

- You can continue to wait for the rabbi, to find out more about the writing from him, but you might waste another hour. If you want to risk waiting, go to page 16.

- You can find out about attacks on Jews, if you haven't already done so, by going to page 11. If you do this, you will have to **add 1 hour to your time score.** Before you go to page 11, **bookmark this page** so that you can return to it afterwards.

- You can return to the synagogue to find out more about the writing from Rachel and Simon, if you haven't already done so, by going to page 14.

You find out about attacks on Jews

Add 1 hour to your time score.

Your self-appointed assistants, Rachel and Simon, ring their mum to tell her where they are. While they enjoy a coffee, taking turns sitting and spinning round in your revolving chair in your office, you get out the dictionaries and encyclopedias. Your Quicksolve assistant staggers in with an armful of books from the library.

This is what you piece together about attacks on Jews, from what the youngsters and the books can tell you.

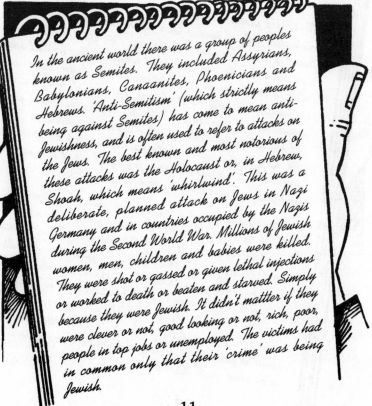

In the ancient world there was a group of peoples known as Semites. They included Assyrians, Babylonians, Canaanites, Phoenicians and Hebrews. 'Anti-Semitism' (which strictly means being against Semites) has come to mean anti-Jewishness, and is often used to refer to attacks on the Jews. The best known and most notorious of these attacks was the Holocaust or, in Hebrew, Shoah, which means 'whirlwind'. This was a deliberate, planned attack on Jews in Nazi Germany and in countries occupied by the Nazis during the Second World War. Millions of Jewish women, men, children and babies were killed. They were shot or gassed or given lethal injections or worked to death or beaten and starved. Simply because they were Jewish. It didn't matter if they were clever or not, good looking or not, rich, poor, people in top jobs or unemployed. The victims had in common only that their 'crime' was being Jewish.

11

Factory production lines in death in 'civilized' Europe: you feel chilled as you think about them. But you're surprised to learn that similar attacks have been going on for hundreds, even thousands of years before that.

Attacks on Jews go back to Bible times, to the days when they were first a people. Despite Nazi attacks on the Jewish 'race', there is no such thing as the Jewish race, because there are white Jews, black Jews, brown Jews — all colours, all races. The Jews are a people identified by their religion or by their having a Jewish mother and being part of a Jewish family.

There are famous cases of English anti-Semitism. The mutilated body of twelve-year-old William of Norwich was found in a wood outside Norwich in 1144. By 1149 the story was around, with not a shred of evidence, that he had been ritually murdered by Jews. Ritual murder doesn't even exist in Jewish teaching or tradition, but that didn't stop the vicious gossip spreading. 'Little St Hugh' was a nine-year-old boy whose body was found in a well in Lincoln in 1255. He may well have simply fallen in and drowned by accident, but the slander that Jews had killed him led to a mob torturing and hanging several local Jews.

Making Jews wear a special badge, like the yellow Star of David, to mark them out for persecution, was not a Nazi invention. As early as 1215 the Christian Lateran Council insisted that Jews had to wear a different sort of hat or badge in order to be noticed. Synagogues are still the target of graffiti or even arson attack by a fanatical minority. Some employ security staff to protect the premises. Some individual Jews have to have their telephone numbe removed from the telephone directory because of unpleasa calls, even death threats.

12

You reflect sadly that this is supposed to be the civilized 1990s. But you also think about the writing on this synagogue wall. There are no Nazi swastikas or anything obviously obscene, insulting or anti-Jewish. The writing isn't even visible to the passing public, since it's on an inside wall. Far from being anti-Semitic, it seems to be very carefully written and therefore some sort of message for the Jews here, or for one of them.

A phone call to the local newspaper informs you that there have been no reported attacks on Jews in this area for many years. You can probably rule out anti-Semitism as a reason for this particular crime.

If you have not yet been to the Levys' house, you have two choices:

• To go there now and wait for David Levy, the rabbi, to get home. To do this, go to page 10.

• To pop back to the synagogue and find out more about the writing from Rachel and Simon, if you haven't already done so, by going to page 14.

If you have already been to the Levys' house, you must return to the other options on the page you came from. If you forgot to mark it, go to the choices on page 10 and pick up the trail from there.

You find out more about the writing from Rachel and Simon

'This is definitely Hebrew?' you ask them.

'Well, the letters are Hebrew, but I'm not sure about the language itself,' says Simon.

'Can you read it?'

'Oh yes, I can read what it says.'

'When did you start learning Hebrew?'

'Well, from being a toddler until teenage, we went to religion class on Sunday morning and for about three quarters of an hour during that class every week we learned Hebrew. Not really to speak it, more to be able to understand what's said and sung in the services here and to sing some modern Israeli songs.'

'The writing's unpointed,' Rachel explains, 'which means it's written without any vowels. All Hebrew's like that and it's written from right to left. You soon learn to put the vowels in as you read it.'

'What does this say in English letters, then, and the right way round?' you ask. Simon jots it down in your notebook:

Mn' mn' tkl uprsn

'What does it mean and what is it doing here?'

'I think you'd do better to discuss that with Dad. Besides, as the rabbi, his Hebrew is brilliant compared to mine!'

If you haven't already been to the Levys' house, you have two choices:

- To go there now and wait for the rabbi to return, by going to page 10.

- To find out about attacks on the Jews, if you haven't already done so, by going back to your office on page 11. If you do this, you will have to **add 1 hour to your time score**, but it might give you a clue to the solution of the case.

If you came here from the rabbi's house, return to the choices on page 10.

15

You continue to wait for the rabbi

At last, you hear the front door shut and Mrs Levy explaining to her husband in a low voice that you are in the lounge. You hear his footsteps as he hurries along the hall and enters the room. He shakes your hand in a nervous pump action. Rabbi David Levy is a friendly person but he has a worried frown on his brow. He waves you back to your armchair.

'I don't know, I don't know,' he mutters to himself, appearing to forget you.

'Rabbi, err, could you please tell me what you make of this?' you ask. Rachel and Simon sit by him to hear what he says.

'I've just got back from an area meeting of rabbis. It was vital to be there. You see, I wanted to know if anyone else had had the writing in their synagogue.'

'And had they?'

'No. That's bad, because it means that the writing is directed specially at us.'

'But what does it say?'

'It says "Mene, mene, tekel and parsin".'

'Is that Hebrew?'

'Not quite. It's Aramaic.'

'What's Aramaic? Is it like Arabic?'

'No, it was the everyday language of ancient Babylon and by the time of Jesus – the one Jew everyone has heard of apart from Moses! – it had become the daily language of the Jews in Israel. Hebrew was used for synagogue services and Aramaic for just about everything else, except when they spoke Greek.'

'But what do the words mean?'

The rabbi sighs. 'The words say "Count, count, weigh and divide".'

16

'Like Maths?'

He laughs a sad laugh. 'In a way. But it's a quotation. The meaning behind those words is terrifying. Terrifying!'

'Why?'

'Because they're from the Book of Daniel.'

'I seem to remember hearing something about Daniel in the lions' den.'

'It's not that part. The book was written to encourage Jews at a time of terrible suffering and persecution. It's the story that these words appear in and the way the story ends that makes it so terrifying. Do you want to know more about it?' He settles back, looking round the room slightly nervously as if something terrible could happen at any minute. 'Can you spare the time?'

You're about to answer him when you happen to glance at the daily newspaper on the coffee table. You see a three-inch headline: the writing on the wall again!

'Well, can you spare the time?' the rabbi asks again.

If you came here from the rabbi's office late on Friday night, go to page 24.

If not, swiftly you must choose what to do next:

- You could hear from David Levy about the Book of Daniel and the quotation. To do this, go to page 20.

- You could pop back to the Quicksolve office and find out about attacks on the Jews, if you haven't already done so, by going to page 11. If you do this, you will have to **add 1 hour to your time score**. Before you go to page 11, **bookmark this page** so that you can return to it afterwards.

- You could make an excuse and go and buy the newspaper to find out what it says about writing on the wall. To do this, go to page 28.

17

The rabbi sits back. In his role as a teacher, which is what the word 'rabbi' means, he clearly intends to give you a good lecture on the Aramaic language. Oh dear! You think of your schooldays with your teachers going on and on about things. There was old Whatsit ... but now you must pay attention to what the rabbi is telling you:

'Well, the Aramaic language is at least as old as the ancient twelve Hebrew tribes – Benjamin, Dan, Reuben and all that lot. But it didn't catch on among Jews in a big way until the sixth century B.C.E., or before the Common Era – what Christians call the sixth century before Christ. You can guess why we Jews don't call i that! Tomb-writing and coins from then on show Aramaic was spreading, and from 500 B.C.E. it was the official language of the Persian empire. By 480 B.C.E. it was being used in the Book of Ezra in our Bible.

'If you're a Christian you might know that Jesus would have spoken Galilean Aramaic, that's Palestinian Aramaic with a northern accent and dialect. Some of Jesus' Aramaic words have been preserved, Christian friends tell me, in Mark's Gospel. The words he used during his crucifixion, or the words he spoke to Jairus' daughter, "Talitha cumi", which mean "Get up, little girl". You can look it all up if you want.

'Aramaic is used in some quite long sections of our Jewish Bible, particularly the Book of Ezra and a large part of the Book of Daniel. That part includes those very words that have been written on our synagogue wall.'

'So it's very important that they're in Aramaic as opposed to Hebrew?' you ask.

'I don't think it's important at all. What matters is that they are an exact quotation from the Book of Daniel. It's what they mean that matters more. The meaning worries me, not the language.'

You swallow hard. Has this lecture on Aramaic been time wasted? But at least you know it's the meaning of the words that matters.

If you came here after checking up on Miriam Solomons, return to page 45.

If not, your choices are now:

- To look around the synagogue for other clues, by going to page 34.

- To question David Levy further about the writing, by going to page 24.

- To ask David Levy about comings and goings at the synagogue, by going to page 42.

19

You hear about the Book of Daniel

There's a mixture of pleasure and worry on the rabbi's face. He's clearly pleased to have a new audience for a story. On the other hand, he's a very anxious man. While Rachel and Simon have a slightly dreamy, distant look that suggests they've heard it all before, you listen very carefully to what he has to tell you in case it contains a vital clue. This is what he says:

'Those words were a terrible sign of doom. You see our Bible, the Jewish Bible, has the same books as the ones Christians call the Old Testament, but not in the same order. Our Bible has three sections: the Torah – by far the most important – the Prophets, and the Writings. The Book of Daniel is in the Writings section, between the Book of Esther and the Book of Ezra. It's a very strange book and there are two things you must understand about it. First, that it was written during a time of terrible attacks on Jews. It was written to encourage them, to give them hope. Orthodox Jews like myself reckon that it was written during the times which it describes, round about 600 B.C.E. I've heard it said by others that it perhaps came from much later, around 168 B.C.E., from the days of the mad emperor Antiochus IV.'

Mad emperors sound interesting. 'Tell me about him,' you say.

'Him?! He called himself Epiphanes: God Known to Us. How about that for modesty? To us it's blasphemy, using God's name like that. Our people nicknamed him Epimanes instead of Epiphanes, a sort of pun. "Epimanes" means "crazy". A man who calls himself God Known to Us must be crazy! Even though they were living in an occupied country inside his empire, our people wanted to go on minding their own business. They wanted to go on living their own lives, causing no trouble, worshipping in our way. But he had to interfere and force the Greek religion on us. It came to a head when he did the Unspeakable.'

Rabbi Levy pauses and shakes his head. What could it have been, this unspeakable thing? As you wonder, you hear the clock on the wall ticking in the silence. It marks the time that is passing. Do you need to get on more quickly, in case something terrible happens while he's rambling on?

If you want to make an excuse and go out and buy that newspaper to see what it says about writing on the wall, go quickly to page 28.

If you don't, read on.

'Well, I will speak of the Unspeakable all the same,' Rabbi Levy continues. Simon exchanges a glance and a wink with Rachel. They'd guessed Dad would keep speaking!

'Antiochus put a statue of the Greek god Zeus, with his own face carved to represent the god's face, inside the holy Jewish Temple at Jerusalem, the house of Almighty God Himself. This is the God who cannot be drawn, who gave us 613 commandments – more as well! – including one that directly forbids making or worshipping images. Antiochus did it to provoke our people. What did Antiochus know? He must have been mad! He provoked God Himself! It was an abomination! An abomination ... and that is exactly what the Book of Daniel calls it in, in chapter 9, verse 27, I think you'll find, and other places too. We had no choice but to fight for our faith and to recapture our Temple.

'The result was a terrible war against the Greeks who had taken over our country. They had armies. We just had faith. For three years, from 168 to 165 B.C.E., our people's sufferings were at their worst as the battle raged. Some people think that the Book of Daniel was written then and bits of it are in a sort of code that the readers would have known but the attackers wouldn't. But we got the Temple back in the end. One of our festivals, the Festival of Lights, Hanukah, remembers how the menorah, the seven-branched candlestick in the Temple, was relit and the Temple made pure again for worship. The festival falls in December – it's a good time in England for a festival of lights.' He pauses.

'Personally, as I said, I think the book had been written long before then, although it would have helped our people in that time of wicked persecution. But you need to know a bit about Daniel. You may have heard the lions' den story, which is in this book? Well, Daniel is a sort of Robin Hood, or King Arthur of the Jewish religion at this time. He interprets dreams, rescues beautiful women, kills a dragon, catches imposters – he's a superman. He stars in at least two other books that survive outside our Bible – the Book of Susanna and the story of Bel and the Dragon ...'

You hear that clock ticking again. You can't sit silent any longer so you interrupt Rabbi Levy and ask: 'Surely, then, a quotation on your wall from this book would be a good sign, with Daniel a Jewish hero and all that? Couldn't it be a kindly practical joke? An offer of hope like the Book of Daniel?'

'Well,' answers the rabbi, and he suddenly looks more serious, 'it depends. You see, those particular words are words of death, if they're aimed at us. I think they worried Danny, when I told him.'

'Danny?'

'Yes, he's the synagogue security officer.'

'Daniel in full?'

'Mmm.'

'And the words, "Count, count, weigh and divide"?'

David Levy's face clouds over. 'I think we've been given a warning. You see, it goes back to the original writing on the wall in the Book of Daniel,' he says.

If you came here from the rabbi's office late on Friday night, return to page 80.

If not, you have three choices:

• To go and interview this Daniel or Danny, the security officer, in case he can help. Wouldn't he have his own keys to the synagogue? To return to the synagogue to look for him, go to page 30.

• To stay and see exactly what David Levy means about the original writing on the wall. After all, he's only given you background to the Book of Daniel so far. He hasn't even got round to explaining the writing itself. To question him further, go to page 24 and take the risk that you'll have to stay here for another hour!

• To ask the rabbi about Aramaic, the language used in the writing, by going to page 18. This too might take you an extra hour. Dare you risk it?

23

You question David Levy further about the writing

'What's the original writing on the wall?' you ask.

'It's in one of the Daniel stories,' explains David Levy, 'and it goes like this. Once upon a time King Belshazzar – he was a wicked foreign king who ruled our people – held a great feast. To this party he invited one thousand nobles and their families. The eating and drinking, singing and dancing went on and on until it was very late at night, or very early in the morning, whichever you prefer! While the guests were over-eating and overdrinking, the king was showing off to them and to his various wives and women who were there. He ordered the servants to bring in the very special gold and silver bowls and cups which his father had stolen from the holy Temple in Jerusalem when he had ransacked it when he was king. Sacred Jewish crockery, in use at a drunken pagan party!

'Well, the story goes that as they were doing this, a human hand – no body attached – suddenly appeared. It began to write on the plaster wall of the palace, just in the place where the best lamplight fell and the words could be most easily seen and read. It would have been right behind the king's head, because he sat with the most important guests at the top table and the lighting focused on him, a bit like the way modern spotlights shine on the stars on stage.

'Imagine it! Half-drunk men and women staring to try to focus their bleary eyes on what was being written on that white plaster wall by the bodiless hand! The king wondering what they were gazing at behind him, then turning to see for himself. He saw it only too clearly and he went white. Deathly white. He dropped his stolen goblet, spilling a flood of red wine

24

across the table. His hands trembled on the table top.
He couldn't keep them still. His knees began to shake.
Beads of sweat gathered on his forehead. He was on
the point of collapse. The whole great hall fell silent.

25

No more din of eating, drinking, shouting and the clatter of cutlery. No sound from the musicians. The servants stood as if in a trance with the serving-dishes in their hands. They were watching the wall where the hand had written and watching the pitiful collapse of the mighty king.

'It was the king who finally broke the awful silence. He struggled to his feet and croaked in a loud shrill voice to send for his magicians, wizards and astrologers at once, to tell him what the writing meant. He was so terrified that he offered a reward of royal robes, a gold chain and the rank of third in the kingdom to any person who could explain it. So from their sleep or their families or their late-night studies, servants fetched his best advisers and wisest people. They claimed to be able to read the stars, but they couldn't read that writing.

'In the end the queen mother – too old to be at the party – heard the uproar through the palace and people running about and shouting in the corridors. She got up, dressed and hurried in to see what was going on. Her clear mind made the best suggestion: fetch Daniel. He was a man famous for common sense, wisdom and knowledge. This Daniel was fetched. He,' and the rabbi stops here with a grin of pride, 'was Jewish. He scorned the king's reward as an unnecessary bribe and explained the writing anyway. He told them that the hand had been sent from God. God was angry at the king's pride, and at the misuse of the Jerusalem holy Temple cups and bowls, and most angry of all not to be honoured by the king.

'"I will read you the words and I will tell you the meaning," Daniel said. "The words say 'Count, count, weigh and divide'. 'Count' means your days are counted, numbered. 'Weigh' means you have been weighed on God's scales and found to be too light. 'Divide' means your kingdom will be divided and

26

given to two other empires."' David Levy pauses to polish his glasses, before he finishes the story.

'And that very same night, in a revolution in the palace, Belshazzar the king was murdered in his bed and replaced by King Darius.' He pauses again and blinks. The room is silent for a moment or two.

'Is the story true?' you ask the rabbi.

He smiles. 'There's a lot of truth in it,' he says. 'There really was a prince Belshazzar – the name means "May Bel (a god of those days) Protect the King". He was the last prince of Babylon and there was a real Darius quite a bit later on. But what worries me is not what happened or didn't happen then, but what might happen now.'

'How do you mean?'

'Look what happened to Belshazzar. Ask yourself, what is the writing on our wall saying about one of us, or all of us in the synagogue?'

'Are you seriously suggesting God wrote it?'

'I doubt very much whether the Lord needs a tin of paint to communicate his message. No, I think it's something more sinister than that, and much more human. You've got to catch this person, before something really terrible happens.'

If you came here from the rabbi's office late on Friday night (via page 16), return to page 80.

If not, you have these choices:

• You could go and interview Danny, the synagogue security officer, if you haven't already done so, by going to page 30. He might have information about how someone could have got into the synagogue.

• You could ask David Levy about comings and goings at the synagogue, in case he knows any more that would help, by going to page 42. Of course, he will take time, so you will have to add 1 hour to your time score if you choose this option.

27

The article starts off like this:

Inside the clipping:

...gland looks set to suffer
...ther major defeat at the
...ds of the tourist eleven in
...ay's test match. With all
...t for 26, which included
...ir Wides and three Byes,
...d the tourist score
...rrently at 416 for one
...mith, who hit the ball
...ice) it is understood that
...e selectors are considering
...icking a new team for the
...ext test match to include 76
...ear old Frank Abbott who
...ised to play for Rutland
...econd XI.

To your surprise you find no further reference to walls, or to writing on them. It dawns on you that the headline means that England cricket looks set for a massive collapse. Lots of people say 'The writing's on the wall' when someone or something is facing disaster. You wonder how the phrase has come to be used like this. So you ring the Quicksolve office and ask your assistant to look up its origin.

A few minutes later, your assistant phones back and says that the phrase comes from the Book of Daniel in the Bible. So do the words on the synagogue wall. No wonder the rabbi is worried!

Now you seem to be getting somewhere. Perhaps Bible phrases are the key to the mystery. Curious, you ask your assistant to find out if many other words or phrases from the Jewish Bible or Christian Old

Testament have become part of everyday language. You are given some examples:

Forbidden fruit (Genesis 3)
Cherub (Exodus 25:18)
Jubilee (Leviticus 25:8–13)
Apple of his eye (Deuteronomy 32:10)
Rule with a rod of iron (Psalm 2:9)
Holier than thou (Isaiah 65:5)
Can the leopard change his spots? (Jeremiah 13:23)

Christian worship has adopted two Hebrew words direct:

'Amen', which occurs many times in the Jewish Bible and means 'So may it be' or 'Let it happen!'

'Hallelujah', meaning 'Praise the Lord'.

These don't help in your search. But your assistant's enquiries have taken time.

Add 1 hour to your time score.

If you came here from the rabbi's office late on Friday night, return to page 80.

If not, your choices are now:

- To interview Danny, the synagogue security officer, by going to page 30.
- To look around the synagogue for other clues, by going to page 34.
- To ask David Levy about comings and goings at the synagogue, by going to page 42.
- To question David Levy further about the writing, by going to page 24.

29

You interview Danny

You find Danny Goldstein in the synagogue office. He is a man of about thirty, with greying hair, slightly stooping and big built. He looks a bit as if he's been poured into his smart dark-blue uniform. A large watch-chain shows that there is an old-fashioned pocket watch in his jacket pocket, with the chain linked in to his lapel. It's rather out of place on a modern uniform complete with peaked cap. He looks worried.

'You look worried.'

'Wouldn't you be? Hardly good for my job prospects, someone sneaking into the synagogue, painting the wall, easy as you like, and getting away with it. I'm supposed to be in charge of security in the place.'

'Why do you think they did that?'

'They've gone to a lot of trouble to do it so carefully and well. I think it's definitely a serious threat. It's no joke, I assure you. I think something terrible's going to happen.'

'To you? To the rabbi? To the building? To the congregation?'

'Who knows? But whoever got in like that once could get in again.'

'Who has keys to the building?'

'Me, of course. Rabbi Levy. Abraham Samuels, he's the warden, a leading member of the congregation. He has one. At the moment we've loaned one to the electrician because we're having some rewiring done. Solomons & Son do all our work. Well, Miriam does.'

'Solomons & Son? Miriam? What do you mean?'

'Manny Solomons was the father who set up the business. He's been dead for years. Frank is the son. He's eighty-six. Miriam is Frank's daughter. She's in charge now. She's about thirty.'

'That doesn't add up.'

'Frank married again after his first wife, Leah, died. Leah ran the plumbing side of the business, but when he married again Esther, his second wife, wanted nothing to do with that. So Miriam, their daughter, eventually was trained in the electrical side and runs it all herself now.'

'Anyone else have a key?'

'No.'

'So there are only four keys: the rabbi has one, you have one, Abraham the warden has one and Miriam the electrician has one?'

'Right.'

'So one of you must have done this, unless someone got in by borrowing a key and duplicating it, or something?'

'That's another of the things that upset me,' Danny continues, 'I'm a suspect.' You ignore that remark for the moment.

'Do you have a plan of the synagogue?'

'Yes, it's in this drawer. We had one done for the fire-regulations inspection.' He takes it out and opens it on the table for you to see.

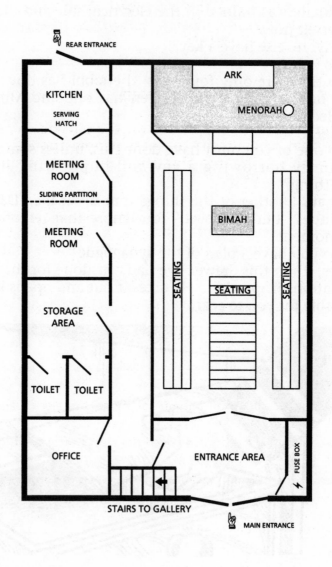

CENTRAL SYNAGOGUE
GROUND FLOOR

REAR ENTRANCE

KITCHEN

SERVING HATCH

MEETING ROOM

SLIDING PARTITION

MEETING ROOM

STORAGE AREA

TOILET TOILET

OFFICE

STAIRS TO GALLERY

ARK

MENORAH

BIMAH

SEATING

SEATING

SEATING

ENTRANCE AREA

FUSE BOX

MAIN ENTRANCE

You study the plan carefully. Rachel and Simon look with interest as well as they haven't seen it before.

'So there are the double doors at the front entrance, the kitchen door and the fire exit from the first floor?'

'Yes, but the fire exit is a one-way door. You can't get in from the outside. There's no outside handle, just a push-bar on the inside.'

'So there are only two doors that the person could possibly have used?'

'Yes, and the same key fits both.'

'Windows?'

'You can see they're barred on the outside. We have to do that, because in the past people thought that Jews were all rich and that there'd be lots of stuff in here worth stealing.'

'Is there?'

'What's here is of religious or sentimental value, not financial. People's families donate scrolls or pointers to read them with, or service books – things like that. But we never keep money here.'

'Mmm.'

You think about this before you make your next choice:

• You could wander around the synagogue and look for other clues, by going to page 34 .

• You could check up on the rabbi, David Levy, as a suspect, by going to page 39.

• You could check up on Miriam Solomons, the electrician, as a suspect, by going to page 44.

• You could check up on Danny Goldstein, the security officer, as a suspect, by going to page 46.

• You could check up on Abraham Samuels, the warden, as a suspect, by going to page 48.

• You could ask David Levy about comings and goings at the synagogue, by going to page 42.

You look around the synagogue for other clues

'We mustn't be late back, Rachel. That's because Shabbat, the Sabbath, starts thirteen minutes before sunset tonight,' Simon explains for your benefit, 'and the candles have to be lit before then. Sunset is traditionally when the Jewish day begins.'

'That's rather odd, isn't it, starting a day at sunset?'

'Not really,' says Rachel. 'No more odd than starting the day at midnight, when it's dark and most people are asleep.'

'Isn't Shabbat rather gloomy and restricted?'

'Not at all,' Simon replies. 'We all enjoy a day of rest from the start of Shabbat prayers, which Mum says at home. Shabbat lasts till Saturday sunset. I admit I do miss the Saturday football, but I can go to the midweek and Sunday matches. And the compensations are really good – it's a day of rest, relaxation, family time, sort of takes us out of the rush of the twentieth century.'

'We like Shabbat,' agrees Rachel. 'It's so peaceful and different. We don't even use the telephone and the lights are on time switches.'

'Really?'

'Yes, but Grandma always goes on about the good old days before time switches when you only had candles and firelight. When they'd gone out you either sat in the dark or went to bed.' Perhaps you feel some sympathy as you reflect that the seven days of the week are becoming just like each other in the rest of the western world now, with shops open every day nearly everywhere.

'Does Shabbat mean I can't carry on with the investigation because I'd offend people?'

'Well, under ordinary circumstances you'd be breaking the commandment by working on Shabbat,' answers Simon. 'The commandment says,' he continues, chanting it off like a times table, '"Observe Shabbat and keep it holy, as I, the Lord your God, have commanded you. You have six days in which to do your work, but the seventh day is a day of rest dedicated to me. On this day no-one is to work." But it is always permitted to work on Shabbat to save life, and if Dad's right, that's just what you might be doing.'

'Do people come here on Shabbat?'

'There's a Friday service and a big service on Saturday morning at 9 o'clock.'

'Will all the Jews from the town be here for the Saturday-morning service?'

'Oh no! Some come every week. Some come less often. Some come hardly at all, just at the main festivals.'

'Could the person responsible for the writing be planning a nasty surprise during the morning service?'

'He could,' Simon starts to say, 'unless "he" is a she.'

'Mmm.' You wander round the ground floor.

'What's the platform here for?'

'It's called the bimah. The Torah – our most special religious book – is read from here.'

'And the Ark is where the Torah scrolls are kept, didn't you say?'

'That's right,' replies Simon.

'Let's undress the old scroll the children practise on!' says Rachel, leading you towards the Ark at the front. Reverently, Rachel and Simon open the double Ark doors. There are lights inside the cabinet and you can see what you guess are a dozen scrolls, wrapped in silk cloths. Simon lifts one out, still wrapped up.

'It's full of symbols,' he tells you. 'Some people say the silver bells on the top represent the sweet sound of

35

the Torah. The breastplate is like the one the high
priest wore in the days of the Jerusalem Temple and
has the symbols of the twelve Hebrew tribes on it. The
crowns on top of the poles the scroll's rolled on are
called in Hebrew 'rimonim', pomegranates, from their

original shape. They're reminders that the Torah is our crowning possession. This silver hand is called a yad. Readers use it as a pointer to keep their place. That way they avoid touching the scroll itself by hand and perhaps soiling it or smearing the ink with moisture in their finger. The yad is always silver. Gold is never used. It led to trouble and the making and worshipping of a golden calf in the days of Moses.' Carefully the youngsters undress the scroll, as unwrapping it is called, and unroll it to show you the inside.

'A Torah scroll has to be handwritten by a professional scribe and the parchment alone can cost several thousand pounds,' says Simon. 'It takes up to a year for one person to copy one in full. The scribe uses traditional materials: parchment made from special animal skin, special vegetable ink and a quill pen made from goose or turkey feathers. The ink doesn't soak in like ordinary pen writing but hardens on the surface of the scroll instead. This means that occasionally letters get chipped and have to be repaired. A completed Torah scroll might cost up to £12 000.'

'But we never throw them away!' Rachel chips in. 'They're used for as long as possible, then they might become practice scrolls for the children, like this one. If they're really unusable we actually bury them in a Jewish cemetery. It's a way of showing respect to God's holy word.'

'Is this worth stealing?' you ask.

'Not really. It's only of use to Jews and they'd know where it had come from.'

'Mmm.' While they carefully put the scroll away, you wander into the kitchen to inspect the back door. Nothing looks out of place. Back in the corridor, you notice the stairs leading to the gallery. This time you wander up the staircase and on to the top landing. Through the door in front of you is the gallery area for women and for visitors.

By this time Rachel and Simon have come upstairs. They explain to you that because this is a traditional or Orthodox synagogue, nearly all of the service is in Hebrew and they follow older customs than some other Jewish groups such as Reform Jews. In Orthodox synagogues, men and women sit separately, musical instruments aren't used, prayers are chanted more often than said, and the main Shabbat service lasts about two and a half hours (but you can go in and out!). In Reform synagogues, men and women can sit together, organs are used, about two thirds of the Shabbat service is in English and it's shorter. Women can read the Torah and be rabbis in Reform but not in Orthodox synagogues.

You're still on the landing looking into the gallery and listening to Rachel and Simon when you happen to notice the fire door. The bar on the inside is firmly down in the locked position. Does this mean that no-one can have entered this way?

You decide to say nothing about this to Danny, the security officer, or even to Rachel and Simon at this point. You don't want anyone else to know too much about how you're thinking – yet. But it does look very much as if the writing on the wall is an 'inside job', by someone who's come in at the kitchen door or through the main entrance using a key. But why?

Choose again:

- You can interview Danny, the security officer, if you haven't already done so, by going to page 30.

- If you have talked to Danny, you can start to check out the key-holding suspects he told you about by going to the list on page 33.

- You can ask David Levy about comings and goings at the synagogue, by going to page 42.

38

You check up on Rabbi David Levy

Rachel and Simon can't help you on this one as you don't want them to know that you're checking their father's background. So you make the excuse that you have to see your assistant and make your way back to the Quicksolve office. In fact your assistant happens to have a Jewish friend – they used to go to school together – and has been talking to her about the people at this synagogue.

You had a vague idea that all local Jews would know one another, as they belong to a minority religious group. You're surprised to discover from your assistant's work on this that there are approximately 300 000 Jews in the U.K. population. Half of them live in the London area. Another large Jewish community is based around Manchester (35 000). There are about 350 synagogues in the U.K., some with very few members and struggling to keep going, some with hundreds. About one in five Jewish children goes to a Jewish school, the others going to any other suitable available school.

Although your assistant's friend doesn't know David Levy, she knows someone whose cousin is a member of his congregation. So you piece together information through this chain of acquaintances and from your assistant's encyclopedia and library work.

As a result of persecutions over many centuries, Jews often had to move to start new lives elsewhere. Many came to the U.K., others went to the U.S.A., and after the Second World War many went to live in Israel. David Levy's family have been living in the U.K. since the 1870s. Like many other Orthodox (traditional) Jews they came from eastern Europe, in their case Poland, to find work in the clothing trade in Manchester. David's great-grandfather and after him his grandfather worked long hours in one of the textile mills for very little pay, sometimes less pay than the non-Jewish workers. His father went into shop work and ended up as the manager and owner of a small tailor's business.

David's earliest synagogue memory, from before he went to infant school, is of the Ner Tamid, the red light suspended from the ceiling in front of the Ark. He is fond of referring to this in his sermons. This is the everlasting light, which symbolically never goes out. Of course even the long-life bulb has to be changed, but the symbol made a great impression on the young David. It was a reminder of the everlasting light of the Torah and of God's presence in the synagogue, whether people are there or not. He used to think about it when he was in bed and the building was locked up – light glowing in darkness.

He was also thrilled by stories of his namesake King David – of David and Goliath fame. King David lived round about 1000 B.C.E. and was to many Jews the ideal Jewish king. Being called Levy or Levi also has significance in the Jewish religion, because it is believed to show that you might be a descendant of the Levites. They served the priests of the old Jerusalem Temple and formed the choir, the Temple security force, acted as doorkeepers and performed other duties. Similarly, people called Cohen or Kohen may be descended from the Temple priests. In Orthodox synagogue services, people named Cohen or Kohen are called up to the bimah to read the Torah first, if they are believed to be descended from the Temple priests. After them the Levis or Levys are called up, then others.

The Levi family were not suprised when David announced that he wanted to become a rabbi. After studying Hebrew and Ancient Oriental Languages at university, he went to Jews College to train. His grandfather was very proud and the old man threw a great party to celebrate.

While he was at Jews College David attended one of the local Orthodox synagogues and met and married Ruth Gould, a member of that congregation. He has moved synagogue once as rabbi, after he saw this post advertised and applied for it successfully. He now has a large congregation and two teenagers of his own, Rachel and Simon, to look after!

There is no hint of scandal or suspicion about David's life that you can uncover. Although he has a key to the building, it seems highly unlikely that he would write a message on the wall of his own synagogue then call you in to investigate it. You are probably safe to rule him out as a suspect, but your enquiries have taken time.

Add 1 hour to your time score.

If you came here from interviewing Danny or checking up on Danny, Miriam or Abraham, next find out more about one of the suspects you haven't already investigated:

- To check up on Miriam Solomons, the electrician, go to page 44.
- To check up on Danny Goldstein, the security officer, go to page 46.
- To check up on Abraham Samuels, the warden, go to page 48.

If you came here after meeting Miriam Solomons for the first time, return to page 50.

If you came here just after the rabbi mentioned the Book of Amos, return to page 51.

If you came here from the rabbi's office late on Friday night, return to page 80.

You ask David Levy about comings and goings at the synagogue

This conversation will take time:

Add 1 hour to your time score.

'Who'd be coming and going at the synagogue during a typical week?' you ask David Levy.

'Well, me for a start. I have an office there and I lead a short daily service at 7 a.m. and another usually at 6.30 p.m. But rabbis are teachers first and foremost and people look to us to explain the Torah. So I'm available at certain times each week in the synagogue office for people to pop in. But you mustn't think I'm in charge of the synagogue. Sometimes I lead the most important part of the service, reading the holy Torah, helped by seven men from the congregation who read blessings before and after the reading. But the Torah might be read by the hazzan. As rabbi I preach the sermon and I try to explain what I think the reading is about and what it means for us in our daily living. The special singer or cantor called the hazzan leads the chanting in the service. With my voice he should do it!

'Of course, I take wedding and funeral services too. Weddings are usually on Sundays in this country since lots of people aren't at work, but in Jerusalem Tuesday is a preferred day because God blessed that day twice in Genesis 1. Funerals take place in the home of the family and at the cemetery, not at the synagogue .. Now where was I?'

'Comings and goings at the synagogue.'

'Oh, yes! Well, I go and do the business side of my work in the synagogue office for a couple of hours each day. Monday is youth-club night. Tuesday is old folk's day, with a sort of social and lunch for elderly members of the Jewish community. On Thursday there's an adult religion class in the evening. On Friday morning the women meet and in the afternoon or evening there's the short service before Shabbat.'

'Was anything different this week?'

'No, I came and went. Danny was around as usual. Oh, we've got Miriam – she's an electrician – in doing some rewiring. I saw her around once or twice and heard her hammering. The shammas has been off ill for several months, so he hasn't been in. He's a sort of caretaker who looks after the special religious objects.'

'Does he have a key?'

'No, Danny lets him in. Then Abraham Samuels – he's the warden – came in and chatted to me once, I think. Yes! He did, because we talked about arrangements for a bar mitzvah next month.'

'Bar mitzvah?'

'That's right. It's when a thirteen-year-old boy becomes "son of the commandment", a religious adult, and reads from the Torah in synagogue for the first time. It's a big family and community event. There's usually a party after.'

'Anything else or anyone else unusual this week?'

'No, no, I'm quite sure there wasn't.' You ask yourself if this points strongly to the writing being an 'inside job'.

Choose one of the following you haven't already done:

- You could look around the synagogue for other clues, by going to page 34.
- You could question David Levy further about the writing on the wall, by going to page 24.
- You could interview Danny, by going to page 30.
- If you have talked to Danny, you could check up on him as a suspect, by going to page 46.
- If you have talked to Danny, you could check up on David Levy as a suspect, by going to page 39.
- If you have talked to Danny, you could check up on Miriam as a suspect, by going to page 44.
- If you have talked to Danny, you could check up on Abraham Samuels as a suspect, by going to page 48.

You check up on Miriam Solomons

It turns out that Frank Solomons – he was the Son in Solomons & Son – actually came and rewired the Quicksolve office a couple of years before he retired. Your boss remembers him well.

Frank worked hard and spoke with much pride about Miriam, the daughter of his second marriage. On several occasions she came and worked with him. At that time she was studying part-time at the local FE college, learning Business Studies and Electrical Maintenance, and working with him part-time to learn from his experience. She is remembered as a bright, attractive young woman, who would never work beyond mid-afternoon on Friday because she didn't want to miss the start of Shabbat. She also stuck strictly to Jewish food rules and surprised the office staff by turning down the offer of a 'bacon buttie' from your boss, as pork is forbidden to Jews.

When Frank retired she took over the electrical side of the business completely and seems to have found plenty of customers inside the Jewish community and outside it. She was loaned a key to the synagogue so that she could get in and out to install some new electrical heaters in the gallery. She has been in and out doing that and testing the circuits for the last couple of weeks.

The gossip your assistant's Jewish friend has picked up confirms that Miriam is bright and hard-working and technically gifted. However, the one subject she crashed at school was French (GCSE result, Grade U) and she was the worst person at Hebrew in religion class in synagogue in living memory. The previous rabbi used to say that it was as well that the Almighty could speak every language, because Miriam never would! She used to reply – when she was twelve and cheekier – that the story of the Tower of Babel (Genesis 6) proved that languages were a curse anyway. She and the old rabbi used to laugh together about it, because he used to joke that he couldn't change a fuse to save his life!

So Miriam's Hebrew is so bad that she couldn't have done the writing on the wall. But the writing is actually Aramaic. And she could have got someone else to do it for her. Can you rule her out?

If you came here from interviewing Danny or checking up on Danny, David or Abraham, choose one of the following you haven't already done:

• Find out more about Aramaic, by turning back to page 18. Before you go to page 18, **bookmark this page** so that you can return to it afterwards.

• Check up on Rabbi David Levy, by going to page 39.

• Check up on Danny Goldstein, by going to page 46.

• Check up on Abraham Samuels, by going to page 48.

If you came here after meeting Miriam Solomons for the first time, return to page 50.

If you came here just after the rabbi mentioned the Book of Amos, return to page 51.

If you came here from the rabbi's office late on Friday night, return to page 80.

You check up on Danny Goldstein

This time you feel on safer ground talking to Rachel and Simon. They willingly tell you all that they know about the synagogue security officer.

Danny has been working at the synagogue for just under a year now. There's something of a question mark about him, because it seems no-one knows much about his family or where they came from except that his parents are dead. He isn't a convert from some other faith, or from no faith at all. He has what some would call a Jewish name, but none of his family live near, or perhaps none are alive. When people in synagogue have tried to ask him about them, he's referred vaguely to the Shoah or Holocaust or changed the subject altogether. Certainly no-one in this synagogue can say they have met a member of his family. He lives alone in a flat just around the corner from the synagogue.

It seems very strange that this community appointed him as security officer when so little was known about him. Apparently he had served in the Army for five years then had worked for a nationally known security firm. He provided references from this firm when he applied for the post, which was advertised in the 'Jewish Chronicle'. You learn to your surprise that most synagogue security officers aren't Jewish like Danny.

46

Danny works long hours at the synagogue and opens and locks it for the daily services, the other meetings and for services on Shabbat eve and Shabbat morning. He is around for the women's group, the rabbi's study group, the old people's club, the weekday crèche, bar-mitzvah and festival preparation in the kitchen, almost everything that goes on. His day off is Monday.

The writing appeared sometime between Thursday evening and Friday morning. You have to keep an open mind on this one.

If you came here from interviewing Danny or checking up on David, Miriam or Abraham, choose another suspect to investigate:

• To check up on Rabbi David Levi, go to page 39.
• To check up on Miriam Solomons, go to page 44.
• To check up on Abraham Samuels, go to page 48.

If you came here after meeting Miriam Solomons for the first time, return to page 50.

If you came here just after the rabbi mentioned the Book of Amos, return to page 51.

If you came here from the rabbi's office late on Friday night, return to page 80.

You check up on Abraham Samuels

A talk to Rachel and Simon in the synagogue office provides background information.

Abraham is the synagogue warden. Also, he paid for the new synagogue candlestick or menorah in memory of his parents, who died in the Holocaust. A menorah is a seven-branched candlestick and symbolizes the one described in Exodus 25:31–37 and the one in the Jerusalem Temple. The original in the Temple burned olive oil. When the Temple was destroyed in 70 C.E. by the Romans, the menorah was taken as part of the plundered treasure to Rome. There the triumphal Arch of Titus, built soon afterwards, shows a carving of it. Jews believe that this menorah should not be copied precisely again – this is a sign of mourning for the destruction of the Temple. However, a menorah is one of the symbols in every synagogue and it is the emblem of the State of Israel. The menorah Abraham Samuels provided is one of this synagogue's treasured possessions.

'What about Mr Samuels' job, though? Is he some sort of caretaker?'

'Not at all! As warden,' Simon explains, 'he's responsible for the general running of the synagogue, but not the religious activities. He chairs the Management Committee and is a senior member of the congregation. The job of warden's like ...'

But Simon's explanation is interrupted as his father rushes into the room. He leans unsteadily on the wall and mops his brow. He is pale and trembling.

'You must come at once. More writing has appeared on the wall,' he gasps. At once, you dash into the synagogue hall. On the same wall, under the original writing, is a second inscription, in the same lettering as the first.

Standing in front of you, looking at the wall in horror, are the rabbi, the security officer and another man whom you haven't met but you guess is Abraham Samuels. There is a puzzled silence, broken by a hammering noise coming from a corner up in the gallery. Leaving the three scared men staring at the writing, you hurry up the stairs, closely followed by an excited Rachel and Simon. What is the banging noise? Is it connected with the writing on the wall?

You rush through the doorway from the landing and out into the gallery corner. There is someone in front of you, crouching on the floor, their back to you, banging something with a hammer. The person stops hammering and turns round. It is a woman in a boiler suit, who has been hammering at a clip to fasten some electrical wiring. Miriam Solomons? She stops and turns round to see who you are.

'Oooh, you didn't half give me a turn,' she says, grinning.

More writing on the wall, and all four suspects in the building at the time.

If you came here from the rabbi's office late on Friday night, return to page 80.

If not, before you ask the rabbi about this new writing, you have the chance to find out the background of any of the suspects you haven't already investigated:

- To check up on David Levy, turn back to page 39. Before you go to page 39, **bookmark this page** so that you can return to it afterwards.

- To check up on Miriam Solomons, turn back to page 44. Before you go to page 44, **bookmark this page** so that you can return to it afterwards.

- To check up on Danny Goldstein, turn back to page 46. Before you go to page 46, **bookmark this page** so that you can return to it afterwards.

- To talk to the rabbi about this second piece of writing, go back downstairs to page 51.

You talk to the rabbi about the second piece of writing

It's much shorter than the other writing. Although you can't read it, it seems to you to be a single word this time. Rabbi Levi looks older as he stands shaking his head at the new inscription.

'What does it say?' you ask.

'It's Hebrew and it says "qayitz".'

'What does that mean?'

'Summer.'

'Summer? There's not much threatening about that!'

'There is if you know where it comes from,' says the rabbi. 'It comes from the Book of Amos.'

If you came here from the rabbi's office late on Friday night, return to page 80.

If not, this could be the start of another ramble by the rabbi, but it might help you understand what's going on here. You have to choose whether to listen to what the rabbi has to say about this writing, or whether to find out more about any of the suspects you hadn't finished checking when you came to see this new writing, or whether to look around to see if anything else has been interfered with in the synagogue:

- To hear about 'summer', whatever it means, from the rabbi, go to page 52.

- To check up on David Levy, turn back to page 39. Before you go to page 39, **bookmark this page** so that you can return to it afterwards.

- To check up on Miriam Solomons, turn back to page 44. Before you go to page 44, **bookmark this page** so that you can return to it afterwards.

- To check up on Danny Goldstein, turn back to page 46. Before you go to page 46, **bookmark this page** so that you can return to it afterwards.

- To check the rest of the synagogue, go to page 56.

You hear about 'summer' from the rabbi

'You must understand,' says the rabbi, 'that throughout the history of our people, God sent prophets to speak to them. These prophets were spokespeople for God. They tried to present his message to the people, whether the people wanted to hear it or not. They felt that they had to tell people when God was not pleased with them, when they had fallen away from his law, when they were worshipping other gods and behaving unjustly. Whatever needed to be said at the time, they said it. Their reward was often to be ignored or laughed at or attacked or even killed. It seems so often that to be Jewish brings not special religious privileges but special troubles, special suffering.

'Well, somewhere round about the middle of the eighth century B.C.E., when there were separate northern and southern Hebrew (or Jewish) kingdoms, one of these prophets, these spokespeople, appeared in the north. He was a southerner himself but we don't know much else about him, except that he was a shepherd and he came from a village called Tekoa.

'It was a time of wealth in the north. There were lots of jobs, money was around, people felt secure, that things were all right. No need to worry. Suddenly this man arrived on the scene and started to preach. He attacked the people for being insincere about their religion, for swindling in their business deals by selling worthless wheat at a high price, for ignoring the poor, even for breaking Shabbat law to trade. He compared the women of the kingdom to the fat cows their husbands kept on the hills! He told them he'd seen visions, visions of locusts and fire. Then there was the vision of a basket full of summer fruit.

52

'In the book in the Bible that's named after him, Amos says, "I had another vision ... In it, I saw a basket of summer fruit ... God said to me the End has come for my people Israel ... The songs in the palace will turn into cries of mourning. There will be dead bodies everywhere. They will be thrown out in silence." I've already told you that "qayitz" means "summer", but you also need to know that the Hebrew for "end" is "qetz". Do you see? Remember, Hebrew is written without vowels. It's a pun. As Amos saw the fruit of qayitz in his vision, he saw it as a sign of the qetz, the end that was coming for the people.'

'But what does it mean here?' you ask.

'I'm not sure. But it means that someone, someone who knows the Jewish Bible and Hebrew and Aramaic well, is playing with us. They're sending us these messages and they're planning something terrible, something really terrible. Dead bodies everywhere, that's what Amos saw.'

'You've got to help us! You've got to help us!' Panic in his face, he grips your arm and pleads for help. But it isn't the rabbi who's speaking now, it's the security officer, Danny Goldstein.

If you came here from finding out more about names, return to page 61.

If not, you now have two choices:

• To check the rest of the synagogue, in case other things have been tampered with, by going to page 56.

• To check Amos's message and whether it came true, by going to page 54. This might help you to see what's going to happen next.

53

You check Amos's message and whether it came true

Back at Quicksolve your assistant has been sorting the library books on the Jewish religion and its history and on the Christian Old Testament, in case you wanted more information. The Book of Amos is in Jewish and Christian Bibles so Amos appears in books about both faiths. You get out a Bible and turn to the Book of Amos. Although it has nine chapters, you discover they're very short compared to modern book chapters and fill only seven pages or so in your Bible. You read them quickly, making notes.

Chapters 1 and 2 are about God's anger with various countries for war crimes, especially Israel who, according to Amos, should have known better.

Chapters 3–8 are taken up with the doom of the northern kingdom, describing Amos's various visions, including the qayitz/qetz one.

Chapter 9 has a terrible climax: the northern temple is destroyed and the people are forced out of their land and homes and sent to live in other countries. A final, strange section, that doesn't seem to fit the rest, talks about a rebuilding of the ruins and return of the descendants of those people, in the distant future.

One of the Bible encyclopedias your assistant has produced for you suggests that this later section was added to the book by someone else many years afterwards. But did any of this happen? You turn now to the Bible background books to check.

✔ There were two separate Hebrew kingdoms after the death of King Solomon, the northern known as Israel and the southern as Judah.

✔ The opening of Amos's book (chapter 1, verse 1) fits him in to the time of King Jeroboam 2 of Israel, who reigned from about 786 to 746 B.C.E., though the person who put together the book of Amos also dates it 'two years before the earthquake', whenever that was.

✔ The great empire of Assyria, some of whose writings and carvings survive on display in the British Museum and elsewhere, did attack the northern kingdom of Israel. Assyria besieged its capital, Samaria, for three years, capturing it in 722 B.C.E., destroying its temple and forcing its people to move to other countries. Evidence outside the Bible supports this.

Was Amos a clever man who spotted all this as likely as Assyria grew more and more powerful or did God reveal it to him? Either way, he got it basically right!

That may mean that the same certainty of doom is in the mind of the person writing on the synagogue wall. Perhaps there's going to be a bomb and the writer is mentally disturbed?

If you came here from finding out more about names, return to page 61.

If you came here from the rabbi's office late on Friday night, return to page 80.

Otherwise, go to page 56 to check the rest of the synagogue.

You check the rest of the synagogue

You can't run round the building, as that would be disrespectful, so you think quickly what's best to do. Of course! Rachel and Simon would notice anything different or altered more quickly than you. So you send them off to look, warning them not to touch anything they see which looks remotely suspicious. It isn't even one minute before they come hurrying back to fetch you.

'Come and look! The memorial board! It's the memorial board!'

You go across to the opposite wall where a large carved wooden board is mounted. It names members of the community who've died, in Hebrew and English writing, and gives the dates of their deaths. Each name is inside a small square on the board, which has the space for more than a hundred names. Next to each name is a tiny light-bulb.

'What's the light for?' you ask.

'Members or friends of the family switch it on for the birthday or anniversary of the death of the person. In the old days you lit a candle,' Simon explains.

'But look at this one!' Rachel points. One of the squares has had the light-bulb removed altogether, and the name of the person has been chiselled out completely.

Miriam Solomons, Danny Goldstein, Abraham Samuels and David Levy have all come across to see what the three of you are looking at. 'Oh no!' exclaims Danny, sitting down, looking faint. 'It can't be!' He covers his face with his hands.

'Time to go,' whispers the rabbi to the others. 'Would you like to come with me?' he asks you.

'Come where?'

'It is nearly time for Shabbat. We must go home to get ready.'

'Home? I thought you prayed here.'

'My friend, the synagogue is the house of assembly, the house of study. We sometimes call it "shul", a Yiddish word a bit like "school", but the Jewish home is the centre of our family and religious life. It will soon be time for Shabbat. We must be home in time. We'd be honoured if you joined us.'

'I'll come with pleasure, but perhaps you could leave me your synagogue key. I'd like a little more time here first.'

The others nod their agreement and go into the porch to go out to their various homes. Rachel and Simon go with their father. You close the door after the last one has left. You are alone in the great building. Returning to the main room, you notice the Ner Tamid, the red light in front of the Ark, more clearly than ever as the daylight is fading. You sit in one of the seats facing the Ark, and try to piece together what you know so far.

You jot each point in your notebook:

1. No big crime has been committed. There's just the two lots of writing on the wall and damage to that one small square on the memorial board.

2. Someone is giving clear warning that something terrible is about to happen. That's obviously what the rabbi and the security officer both believe. But this is one of Quicksolve's most unusual detective cases, because we haven't got a major crime — yet. We haven't got a criminal either, and we haven't got a victim for sure.

3. It is highly likely that the person responsible for what has happened so far has a key to the synagogue and can get in and out when they like.

4. The clue to discovering the criminal may lie in finding out who is the intended victim. Is the intended victim all the members of the synagogue, or just one of them? Not all of them would understand the writing — those who aren't much good at Hebrew wouldn't. How does the defacing of the memorial board fit in? Whose name appeared on the blanked-out square? Miriam Solomons, as an electrician, probably has a chisel and could have done it. But her Hebrew isn't good enough for the writing on the wall. In any case, surely there's a tool kit for repairs containing chisel somewhere in the building. Danny Goldstein woul know about that. Come to that, the rabbi would know abo it, and so would someone as important in the community Abraham Samuels. Anyway, whoever took the trouble bring paint for the wall could equally have brough chisel to chip out a name.

Whose name was there? Do they have relatives who still come to the synagogue? Why would someone bother to attack a name? Is there some sort of revenge going on here?

You must choose what to do next:

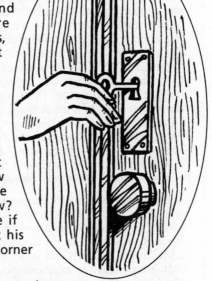

• Are you going to join the rabbi and his family for the start of Shabbat? By doing so you might find out about this missing name and you'll certainly learn more about Jewish customs. Besides, you're hungry and need a rest and a meal. To visit Rabbi Levy's home, drive quickly to page 66 for Shabbat will soon begin.

• Danny Goldstein, the security officer, lives just around the corner. He's nearer. He might tell you all you need to know about the defaced name more quickly. Or would he know? You'd be wasting your time if he didn't. To visit Danny at his flat, walk briskly round the corner to page 62.

• If you want to find out more about names and their meaning, in case it explains why this one has been removed, go to your office on page 60.

Whatever you choose, do remember to lock the synagogue door as you go. You don't want anyone else breaking in.

You find out more about names

Back to the books which your assistant has collected and are now hiding your desk top from view. With the help of a cup of coffee and time to look through them, you discover some surprising things about names.

In the ancient world, including ancient Hebrew society, every name had a meaning and it was believed that someone's name was a clue to their nature. Some names came from animals, e.g. Rachel (Ewe) or Deborah (Bee). When the modern State of Israel was established in 1948, the prime minister took the name Ben-Gurion: Son of the Young Lion. Other Hebrew names were adopted by Jews in Israel as the Hebrew language was brought back for everyday speech and not just synagogue use. These included Baron (Strong) and Yadin (He Will Judge). In ancient times, it was thought that as you got to know someone more closely, you discovered both their personal name and their nature. We still call our close friends by their first names – not Mr, Ms or Mrs – and for our closest friends, or sometimes in families, we invent private nicknames known to only a very few people. Even now, names matter.

The Hebrews believed that there were 72 names for God himself. He wasn't just 'God'. One famous name for God in Hebrew is spelt YHWH. But when Moses asked what it was, he was given not God's name, but a reminder of God's power: 'I am Who I Am' (Exodus 3:13). To the Hebrews and later the Jews, God's name was so sacred that it was never pronounced aloud. Instead they said 'Adonay' or 'the Lord' or 'the Almighty' rather than using God's personal name. So, over hundreds and thousands of years, people forgot how to pronounce YHWH, partly because Hebrew has no vowels. But they didn't want to use God's holy name aloud anyway. It's modern people who are curious about how it was spoken.

Jesus, as a Jew, referred to God's name in what Christians call the Lord's Prayer: 'Your name is holy', or in older translations, 'Hallowed be thy name', a phrase from a Jewish prayer called the Kaddish. But he never pronounced God's name. Today, Orthodox Jews prefer not to write even the word 'God' and so write 'G-d' instead. They don't pronounce it.

Names had such meaning and tradition that it was important for a person's name to be passed on to their children and their children's children. This was one way in which you 'survived' death. Your name lived on. So in ancient society, having no children to carry on the family name was a disaster. In more modern times it was thought vitally important to preserve the name of a dead person. Some Jews therefore deliberately name a baby after a dead member of the family, hoping that their memory will guide the youngster. Others name children after a living member of the family in the hope that she or he will become a model for them. The dead are also named on gravestones in special Jewish cemeteries, on memorial boards, perhaps in gifts dedicated to the community such as a scroll or piece of furniture.

The horror of the Holocaust or Shoah (the Hebrew word for 'whirlwind') is that so many people disappeared without trace, even their names were lost. Yad Vashem, which means 'Hand and Name', is the (Hebrew) name of the Holocaust museum and memorial shrine built in Jerusalem to remember them. In the children's memorial at Yad Vashem, the names that are known are read aloud. G-d himself, Jews believe, remembers the dead.

Names ... You sit pondering about these things. Why did Danny Goldstein panic about the writing? Why did Danny Goldstein say, 'Oh no! It can't be!' when he saw the memorial board? By defacing the memorial board, did someone try to attack the Goldstein parents' names? Are Danny Goldstein and his dead parents the targets of the attack? Does that explain his jumpy, suspicious behaviour? But who would want to get at him and why?

Your choices are now:

• To visit Danny at his flat, by going to page 62.

• To find out more about the second piece of writing, 'summer', if you haven't already done so, by going to page 52. Before you go to page 52, **bookmark this page** so that you can return to it afterwards.

• To check Amos's message if you haven't already done so, since the words there seem so vital, by going to page 54. Before you go to page 54, **bookmark this page** so that you can return to it afterwards.

You visit Danny at his flat

You're curious about Danny, because in a way he comes from your world, the world of security, of crime prevention. You wonder what sort of flat a security officer might live in. Will it have a tiny spy-hole in the door, a closed-circuit TV camera, lots of bolts and locks on the door, like a sort of giant safe?

You arrive at the door of the ground-floor flat to find it – much to your surprise – ajar. By the doorstep are two large tins of paint. Perhaps he was bringing them in from the car and they were too heavy to carry further so he left the door open. A radio is blasting out pop music, so although you ring the bell, you can't make yourself heard. It seems a strange way for someone to start Shabbat, music blaring like this. You still can't get anyone to hear the bell, so you push open the door and wander in.

It's a small flat, with a living-room and kitchen in one. There is an appetizing smell of cooking, which reminds you that you feel hungry. Bacon and eggs have recently been cooked, and presumably eaten, because greasy dishes are piled in the sink in a bowl of washing-up water. That strikes you as odd. Bacon in a Jewish house?

'Hello!' you call out.

'Who's there?' a suspicious voice calls back from the back. 'If you're selling something, go away. I'm trying to get the decorating started.' Decorating? Hard work? Work on the Jewish Shabbat? You think of the commandment. Come to think of it, most Orthodox Jews wouldn't wash up on Shabbat – or even play a computer game – as that would be viewed as work. Something is very suspicious here.

You must decide immediately what to do next:

• Should you leave the flat quickly before Danny Goldstein comes into the room and discovers you're there? In that case, you could hurry to your car and drive round to the Levys' home in time for the Shabbat meal, where you might find out more about what you have seen here. To do this, move to page 66.

• Do you want to stay and question Danny when he appears? To stay, turn to page 64.

63

Danny still doesn't appear, so you walk around the room. You stop to look at his bookshelves. There are lots of books about the Second World War, which must be an interest of his. Surprisingly, there are no books about the Jewish religion and no Hebrew books or Bibles around – you'd recognize these now, after seeing the writing on the synagogue wall. While you're staring at the shelves, Danny walks into the room, paintbrush in hand.

'What on earth ...?' he starts to say, but then recognizes you. 'Oh, it's you.' You get a strange feeling that he is relieved, relieved that you're not somebody else, but at the same time not at all pleased to see you.

'How did you get in?' he shouts above the music, very surprised.

'Through the door,' you coolly shout in reply, 'which you left open.' He turns off the music. The silence is strange and startling after so much noise. To your surprise he goes and examines the door, as if he didn't leave it open and can't understand how you appeared in his lounge. He looks very thoughtful about something.

'You just walked in?' he asks, as if he doesn't believe you.

'Mmm.' He says nothing but sits down on the settee.

'I thought Jews didn't eat pork,' you say, looking in the direction of the washing-up in the bowl.

'That's none of your business, coming in here like this, asking questions,' he says.

'You said you were pleased enough to get my help in the synagogue,' you reply. 'They can't be thinking you're very good security with two break-ins now.' He rests his paintbrush on a newspaper to stop it marking the coffee table.

'Well,' he says ungratefully, 'let's just say I'm not as strict as that lot are, that's all. Don't you go telling them, mind. I'm just decorating the bathroom.'

'Why aren't you at a family meal for Shabbat?' you ask.

'Two reasons: one, I've no family; two, I've no wish to go, that's why. Lots of people invite me, but I don't want to go, that's all.'

'The defacing of that memorial board,' you continue, 'whose name was wiped out? Why did it upset you?' The question has more effect than you expected. He actually changes colour, before your very eyes, and goes paler. He seems very tense.

'I suppose you'll nosey it from someone else,' he says, 'if I don't tell you. It's my parents' names he's taken out, that's who.'

'He?'

'You what?'

'You said "he".'

'Just a manner of speaking, that's all.'

'Why should anyone want to remove your parents' names from the board?'

'Don't ask me! Ask whoever's done it! That's what your job's supposed to be, isn't it? Why don't you go and do it?'

You get up to go. He's clearly in no mood to co-operate further. What do his behaviour and panic at the synagogue mean? Unless Danny's lying, you have discovered the victim.

Outside on the pavement you must choose what to do next:

- You could see the rabbi about this, by joining the Levy family for the Shabbat meal on page 66, even though you're late.

- It also occurs to you that there's at least one suspect you know very little about, and that's Abraham Samuels. You could ring him from your car-phone to ask if you can visit his house and talk to him yourself, by going to page 73.

You join the Levy family for the Shabbat meal

As you're about to ring the Levys' doorbell, you notice a small rectangular box on the doorpost. It is about 8 centimetres long and 2 centimetres wide. What might this be? Simon welcomes you at the door and you find David Levy, his wife Ruth and Rachel assembling in the dining room to welcome 'Queen Shabbat'.

It isn't as late as you thought, although Rabbi Levy hurried off from the synagogue leaving you there some time ago. He left early because it is his passion not to be late for Shabbat, which would break the commandment. This means that instead of being late, you're just in time. Rachel tells you that during the short days of winter, the children are allowed to leave school early on Friday afternoon, in time to be home just before sunset and the start of Shabbat. You think how you'd have enjoyed leaving school at about 3 o'clock in the winter months.

Simon and Rachel explain that they've been busy beforehand preparing food, bathing, putting on their best and favourite clothes and setting up the video recorder to tape programmes they want to watch after

Shabbat is over. Even switching the TV on and off is unnecessary work so they avoid it. Much to your surprise – because you thought it might be dull – you find all four of them enthusiastically looking forward to this day. They enjoy it as a time together for an unhurried meal and talk, a time for prayer and a time of rest and recreation. 'Re-creation' is a good word for it, since they explain to you that God rested on the seventh day from his work of creation, according to the Torah.

Watching TV, going to a cinema or disco, doing homework, playing sport, reading business letters such as bills are suspended in order to enjoy Shabbat. An ancient rule prohibiting making or extinguishing fires is interpreted by some traditional Jews to include turning heaters or lights on and off. At least time switches can now be used and set in advance. Behind all this detail is a vitally important idea: Shabbat is intended to be a day without work or worry. Equally the most traditional Jews agree that it must be broken if life is in danger.

Now Ruth lights the Shabbat candles on the table as a symbol of joy and warmth coming into the home. She says with Rachel the prayer of blessing: 'Blessed are You ... who commands us to kindle the Shabbat light.'

As soon as this blessing has been spoken, Shabbat is held to have arrived. There is wine and bread on the table and pleasure on the faces of the family. You feel privileged to share this special time.

David begins the Kiddush, a Hebrew prayer. Simon

whispers to you that it is a mixture of thanking God for the day, for creation, and for rescuing the Hebrew people from Egypt. Rachel explains that the prayers aren't blessing the food – they're blessing God for it.

Simon tells you that the two loaves on the table are hallah bread. They commemorate the special bread called the Bread of the Presence that used to be kept at the Jewish Temple at Jerusalem. They're also a reminder of the manna that was given to the Hebrews to eat during their desert wanderings. There are *two* loaves to represent the double helping of manna that God gave the Hebrews each Friday morning so that they didn't have to gather another portion the next day – Shabbat. The loaves also represent two commands: 'Remember Shabbat' and 'Keep Shabbat'.

The hallah bread is baked in a sort of plait. Simon explains that the three strands represent God, the Torah (or religious law) and Israel. The bread is sprinkled with salt to remember how in the Book of

Genesis in the Bible, the first people had to earn their bread by 'the sweat of their brow' – sheer hard work.

Hebrew songs are sung at various points in the meal. You can pick out in the Hebrew the family's greeting to each other: 'Shabbat shalom', meaning 'A peaceful, happy Sabbath'.

Sharing this Shabbat meal makes you realize quite suddenly three special things about the Jewish religion. It has an ancient and treasured past, which is often recalled in readings and rituals. Its roots lie in home and family life – being a Jew is nearly always a home and family affair. It is full of symbols – all sorts of things to touch or taste that stand for important beliefs or events in the past and present.

Tomorrow morning the family will walk the short distance – a 'Sabbath day's journey' – to the synagogue for the main Shabbat service. A journey of 2000 cubits, roughly 1300 metres, is permitted when travelling outside a town, any distance is permitted within it. So London Jews can go further on Shabbat than Bournemouth ones! Shabbat will end after sunset on Saturday with a goodbye ritual. Using a special plaited candle and spices such as cinnamon or nutmeg, the family will say farewell to Shabbat but take its sweet smell out into the new week in the home again. But that lies ahead.

Now you have an opportunity to talk to the Levy family. The rabbi has already reassured you that it is permitted to work on Shabbat to save life, and that this is what you might well be doing if there is a murder or bomb attack or violent crime about to take place.

'Tell me about the missing name-plate on the memorial board,' you ask.

'Well,' the rabbi begins, 'it names the Goldstein parents – Danny's mother and father.'

'Were they much loved members of the community?'

'Frankly, no!' You gasp in surprise.

'We never knew them,' the rabbi continues. 'I never met his father. He was dead before Danny came to this job just under a year ago. His mother never came to synagogue, but he told us she was ill, then months later he said she'd died. He paid for the small plaque that was there on the board.'

'Did she live near here?'

'No, she lived in London. I don't think I've ever heard him say exactly where.'

'Which synagogue did she go to?'

'I don't know. I don't think he ever told us that either. It's funny, that, because we might well not have known her, but we'd have been bound to have known her synagogue. I'd probably have known her rabbi too.'

'What about the rest of his family?'

'He doesn't speak of any. I don't know where he goes on Shabbat or for the meals during festivals like Pesach – Passover. Lots of our people have invited him, including us, but he likes to keep himself to himself. I think people have vaguely assumed he's around in the synagogue for some of the time.'

'Does he take a turn at reading in the service?'

'No, he's always declined, but he's not the only one. Some people are shy or don't think their Hebrew's up to it. It's written without vowels, you know. In any case, during prayer he has to be on duty at the synagogue entrance for much of the time.'

'Is there anyone who would know more about him or his family?'

'Well, Abraham Samuels might. He chairs the Management Committee and they organize the appointment of a security officer. Come to think of it, he interviewed the candidates. He might know the family because he's done a lot of research into recent Jewish family trees. He's trying to track relatives of his who were victims of the Shoah. Both his grandparents disappeared, and two uncles, an aunt and his parents.'

'Just a minute, I'm not with you. Whose parents?'

'Abraham Samuels'. He was born in 1933 and in 1938 both his parents were taken.'

'Where?'

'Treblinka, I think. In Poland. The Nazis didn't kill them in Germany.'

'How did he escape?'

'When the SS came for his parents, he was playing in the garden. They didn't bother to stay and search the house and garden. When he came into the house, they'd gone. He never saw his parents again. Think of that! To lose both your parents like that, a little boy out playing. But he was lucky. The neighbours hid him. Most wouldn't have dared, for the penalty was to be sent to a death camp yourself if you were caught. After a few months he was smuggled out and sent to England.'

It occurs to you that Abraham Samuels is a suspect you don't know much about and you ought to meet. The Levys think he might go on from his Shabbat meal to the synagogue, so if you are willing to disturb him you might find him there. Apologizing to the Levys for leaving early, you go out into the hall. Before you open the front door, you remember the rectangular box screwed to the doorpost. Could it be another hidden message that someone has put on the rabbi's door?

You now have three choices:

- If you want to risk delaying yourself by asking the rabbi about the box on the doorpost, turn to page 72.

- If you want to try to catch Abraham Samuels at the synagogue for a private word, turn to page 75.

- If you want to use your car-phone to ring Abraham Samuels, in case he's still at home, turn to page 73.

You ask about the box on the doorpost

'Oh, that,' says David Levy, smiling. 'That's a mezuzah. It's got a little prayer on a piece of paper inside. Well, it's a little prayer with a big thought, our prayer the Shema.'

'Shema?'

'That's the first word in it in Hebrew. It means "Hear" or "Listen" and the prayer starts "Hear, O Israel, the Lord your God, the Lord is One". Jews believe there is only one God.'

'Isn't that something they share with Christians?'

'Yes, and Muslims and Sikhs, so I understand. All these faiths have lots of differences, but they agree that there is only one God.'

'So the mez..., mez..., err...'

'Mezuzah.'

'Ah yes, mezuzah – the mezuzah doesn't contain a secret message?'

'The Shema is the best-known prayer in the Jewish faith. Nothing secret about it at all. As we go into the house we touch the mezuzah to stand for taking the prayer in with us. I'll open the case and show you the scroll inside with the prayer on it if you like, when Shabbat's over.'

'Thanks. I'll look forward to seeing it then. But now I must try to get hold of Mr Samuels.'

- If you came here from Abraham Samuels' house, go to page 75.

- Otherwise, use your car-phone to ring Abraham Samuels, by going to page 73.

You ring Abraham Samuels

You dial the number. The phone keeps on ringing. You dial again. No-one answers. Surely someone's at home for Shabbat? You try again. The phone still just keeps on ringing ... of course! You realize that you've not been applying what you've learnt about Shabbat. If Abraham Samuels or any member of his family is at home, they won't answer the phone, nor would they use it to make a call unless it was a 999 call to save life.

You've got to either drive round to Abraham Samuels' house or go and see whether he's gone on to the synagogue.

- To visit Abraham Samuels' house, go to page 74.
- To look for Abraham Samuels at the synagogue, go to page 75.

You visit Abraham Samuels' house

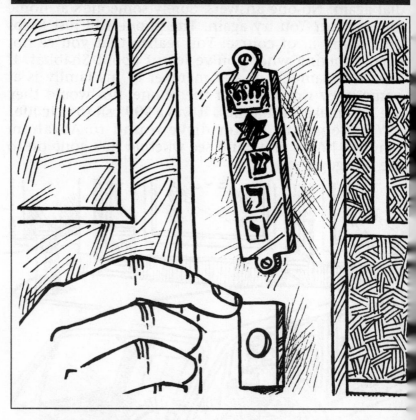

You ring the doorbell but no-one answers. No lights are on. It looks as if Abraham Samuels is not at home.

- If you don't know what the strange box on the doorpost is and want to find out, go back to the Levys' house and see if they can help, by going to page 72.

- Otherwise, return to the synagogue to look for the slightly mysterious and definitely hard to track down Abraham Samuels by going to page 75.

You look for Abraham Samuels at the synagogue

Back at the synagogue, you realize you've by accident kept the rabbi's key, so you can get in without knocking or letting anyone else know you're there. It is now dark. Shabbat evening is well established. Tomorrow local Jews will be walking to the morning service here and the rhythmic chanting of the Hebrew prayers will begin.

You can't see any lights on inside as you let yourself in through one of the double front doors. There is a rustle in the entrance porch. You jump. It's just notices on the board that you've brushed against as you walked past. Quietly you enter the main hall. In the darkness only the Ner Tamid burns red above the Holy Ark. You can faintly see the Commandment tablets on the wall above the Ark in the red glow.

You decide to go through the hall and into the corridor to the synagogue office. As you quietly walk down towards the bimah, you become aware of a lone figure sitting on one of the seats near the front, facing the Ark. You can see the silhouette of a head and shoulders and the hint of a yarmulkah (skull-cap), showing it is a man.

You wonder who it could be. The rabbi? But he can't have beaten you here because he'd be walking on account of Shabbat. Simon? He couldn't either. Danny Goldstein? But would he be in so late and sitting silent like this? Miriam Solomons? Surely she'd be in the women's gallery. A cleaner? But they wouldn't do cleaning work on Shabbat of all days. Might it be Abraham Samuels himself? There's only one way to find out, but dare you? You're tempted to tiptoe back to the porch and leave as silently as you arrived.

You decide not to be a coward, and to confront the mystery figure. Although you try to walk quietly, your feet seem to clomp, clomp, clomp as you walk to meet the stranger. There is no chance of disguising your approach. As you get nearer he – for you can now see for certain that it is a man – turns round, rather alarmed. That's because the building is alarmed and he is astonished to see a stranger inside without the alarm system in full shriek!

'How did you get in here?'

'I've borrowed the rabbi's key,' you reply, showing him the key in proof of your story. 'I saw you earlier in here, didn't I, when the second writing was found?' He nods. He is Abraham Samuels.

'I'm from Quicksolve,' you say, pulling out your ID card, 'and I'm making some enquiries about the writing on the wall.' He nods again.

'I wonder if you can help me?'

'That depends what you want to know.' You can see
his isn't going to be the easiest of interviews. He's not
iving much away.

'What do you make of the writing?'

'It's been very well done. The writer knows his – or
er – Bible well.'

'But what does it mean?'

'Well, the first piece is from the Book of Daniel and
means ...'

'No, I didn't mean that. I meant, why do you think
's been put there?'

'Oh, I'm sure it's a warning.'

'A warning?'

'Certainly. Don't you think that's obvious? The
erson who saw the original writing, in the Book of
)aniel, was dead within hours. The nation that Amos
varned about qetz – an end – ended within a few
ears.'

'But is it aimed at one person or the whole
ommunity?'

'One person, I should say. Mmmm. Definitely.'

'Why do you say that?'

'It's too obscure to be aimed at the whole
ommunity. Besides, who'd want to do that? If it's a
unatic anti-Jew they wouldn't go to the trouble of
reaking in to write a threat, would they? They'd paint
t outside. They'd also paint it in English. And what
eason would a Jew have to attack the whole
ommunity?'

'So who do you think it's aimed at?'

'Oh, I think you'd know if you could find out
nough about the background of the people who come
iere.'

'How can I do that – and have I the time?'

'Well, I doubt whether you've much time, but then
ou might not have as far to look as you imagine.'

'Do you think I've already met the intended victim and the person who's going to do whatever it is?'

'I'm sure you have.'

'Well, who are they?'

He chuckles. 'Mmmm. Well, that's not for me to say, is it? It's only a matter of whether you can beat the disaster before it happens.'

Is he guessing? Or does he know more than he's willing to tell you? How can he be so sure that you've already met the intended victim and the criminal? Is he one of them? If he were the victim, wouldn't he tell you? Perhaps that means he's the criminal. But what evidence do you have? There hasn't even been a crime, apart from the writing and the defacing of the memorial. You expect that Abraham, as a senior member of the congregation, knows Hebrew well. He could have done the writing. He has a key. Perhaps most puzzling of all, why isn't he at home for Shabbat? Or is it because he's warden that he's here?

Perhaps this is the time to go home and do some rethinking, so that you can have a rest and be back in good time for the service on Saturday morning.

Think about it! You have two choices:

- To go home and have a good night's sleep, ready for an early start tomorrow. To do this go to page 79 in good time for the Shabbat morning service.

- To stay in the synagogue all night to think through carefully everything you have seen and heard, and to keep an eye out in case more things start to happen in the night. To do this, go to page 80.

You inspect the synagogue before the Shabbat morning service

Your heart is beating fast as you enter the main hall. There's a feeling of dread hanging over the place. Is today the day when something's going to happen? You tell yourself to be careful! Your first action is carefully to check the whole building for signs of change.

You walk round slowly, inspecting the scene: first the hall, then on to the side rooms. There's a sort of brooding silence. Yet nothing seems out of place. You find yourself tiptoeing around in case anyone's there – while rather hoping that they aren't! But before you can complete your search of the side rooms, you hear low voices in conversation. The sounds are coming from the direction of the entrance porch. People are starting to arrive for the service. You're not going to be able to check any further now because you need to watch who's coming in and what's happening.

You have two choices:

- To go up onto the landing outside the women's gallery to watch the service, because you'll get a good view from there, by turning to page 82.

- To see if you can catch Rachel or Simon as they arrive and find out from them more about Abraham Samuels, by waiting in the porch on page 86.

79

You stay in the synagogue all night

You wander into the kitchen and help yourself to a fruit juice from the fridge. It is cold and helps to keep you awake as you start to think through the strange events that are happening around you. You take your drink back into the rabbi's office and sit in the armchair he saves for visitors. You feel safer in there than in the hall or the gallery. Has Abraham Samuels left the building? Are you alone? You decide not to bother to look. You know that he knows that you know that he's there! And he knows that you know that he knows that you know he's there. If only you knew as much about the solution to the case!

Staying up like this gives you a chance to contact your assistant at Quicksolve. You could ring them, on their home number now, if you want them to check information or find out more about anything or anyone you've missed. You also have the opportunity to remember conversations you've had earlier on in the day.

You can choose to visit or revisit as many of the pages listed below as you wish, but you must **add 1/2 hour to your time score** for every clue you visit which you have already visited earlier in the investigation. This represents your thinking time. Before you go to any of the pages listed, **bookmark this page** so that you can return to it afterwards.

- To read about the original writing, go to page 16 then to page 24. (This counts as one clue, not two.)
- To read about the second writing, go to page 51.
- To read about the Book of Daniel, go to page 20.
- To read about the Book of Amos, go to page 54.

- To read about the 'Writing on the Wall' article in the newspaper, go to page 28.

- To read about David Levy, go to page 39.

- To read about Miriam Solomons, go to page 44.

- To read about Danny Goldstein, go to page 46.

- To read about Abraham Samuels, go to page 48.

When you have finished looking at the clues (if any) you want to check out, read on.

You feel dozy as you sit in this cosy armchair in the rabbi's office with your glass of fruit juice and your thoughts. You slide into an uneasy sleep. You start to dream. Your assistant is dancing around balancing library books in each hand and on the head ... Your old school teacher is telling you off for getting 5% in a test on Aramaic ... The rabbi is telling you he thinks you're really the criminal ... Rachel and Simon are opening the doors of the Holy Ark – but the scrolls are gone and it is completely empty ... The Goldstein parents have committed some dark deed that has been discovered by the person who defaced their names ... Someone is choking you ... Someone is choking you! Aaaargh!

Your head is on the desk. Wire is round your neck. You must fight! You wake up to find that you must have dozed off with the phone in your hand. You remember making a late call to your assistant. You must have dropped the handpiece, winding the cable round your neck as you dozed. The room is empty. No-one is strangling you. It was a dream.

You look at your watch. It is early morning: first light outside. Rather sore after a night in the armchair, you get up and walk around, then get ready to inspect the premises before the Shabbat morning service.

Turn to page 79.

You go up onto the landing to watch the service

You're pleased to see Miriam Solomons in the gallery and she comes across to the doorway to welcome you and make you feel at home.

'I can't translate what all the Hebrew in the service means,' she whispers, 'but I can tell you the main outlines of what's going on. My service book has the words in Hebrew and English to follow too.'

There's a hum of conversation going on. In the gallery there are lots of women and girls. You can recognize the married women because by Orthodox Jewish custom they cover their heads, using scarves or hats. The ground floor is about half full of men and boys. Those over thirteen each wear a fringed prayer-shawl and yarmulkah (skull-cap).

'Is a prayer-shawl compulsory?' you ask.

'For men and boys over thirteen, yes,' Miriam replies. 'It's called a tallit and has four tzitzit or white knotted strands, one in each corner.'

'What for?'

'The stripes on the tallit are often blue: standing for heaven. The white is for purity. If it wasn't Shabbat they'd have to wear tefillin as well: two small black boxes strapped onto the arm and onto the forehead. They contain the Shema, our prayer that starts with the words "Hear, O Israel, the Lord your God, the Lord is One".'

'On your forehead? A box?'

'It stands for the words of the prayer entering your whole person. In Deuteronomy 6 in the Torah, it says about God's word being a sign on your hand and frontlets between your eyes. Men get used to tying on tefillin, like putting on a tie, really.'

On the raised area in front of the Ark you see Rabbi Levy in one seat and another man, the hazzan, sitting in the seat opposite. Miriam explains that the hazzan, or cantor, leads the chanting parts of the service. Rabbi Levy is wearing a black gown over his suit and a traditional hat. Miriam explains that Reform and more liberal Jews have simpler services and simpler clothing, but all men cover their heads. She adds that she likes the ceremony and dignity of this service but that she doesn't understand much of it.

You find yourself drifting away into thoughts about the writing, which is on the ground-floor wall opposite. The synagogue is warm, the rhythms of the chanting are mysterious and sad. You didn't sleep very well last night, and you go into a sort of day-dream in which you're aware of Miriam greeting her friends as they arrive: 'Hello Susie ... Leonie ... Hannah ... Isabel ... Sylvia ...'

You wake up from your day-dream in time to see the Torah scroll being carried in procession from the Ark, round the ground floor. People are leaning out of their seats to touch or to kiss it as a sign of respect. Those carrying it mount the steps of the bimah as the prayers that prepare for the first reading are being chanted. Carefully the silver bells, the breastplate and the covers are removed. The scroll is cleverly rolled to the right part for the reading.

The first reading is about to begin. You're full of admiration as you remember that the reader will have to read the Hebrew from right to left, with a different alphabet, and no vowels, and that he's been reading like this from childhood. In fact the section from the religious law is more chanted or intoned than read. Again you're impressed to be witnessing a form of worship that is thousands of years old. You scribble on your notepad.

ntls ht s thw
gntrw ht t
?llw ht n

84

A woman in the gallery opposite glares at you. She doesn't know who you are and assumes that you're a visiting student writing notes. By doing so you would be breaking Shabbat, so you put your notepad hurriedly away and look back at the reader. You wonder how many people could read your doodling in backwards English, putting the right vowels in. Meanwhile, down below you the Torah is being read as quickly as you read a newspaper. Practice must be part of it.

You note that the key people in this case are all around you. Rachel has come in and is with her mother Ruth two rows behind you in the gallery. Simon is downstairs. Abraham Samuels is in his place. Rabbi Levy is at his seat. Danny Goldstein is ... is missing. That's odd. You would have expected him to be present for at least part of the service, even if he has to guard the door at the beginning. He's nowhere in sight. You've noticed that people have gone in and out at various points in the service. When you asked Miriam about it she smiled and said:

'What do you expect? Nearly three hours is a long time. You might need the toilet! Or you might want to take small children out for a break. Even on Saturday morning we don't need to be here every second. It's not disrespectful to pop out. More disrespectful not to come at all!'

You have to make a choice:

- You could search the rooms at the side, to see if you can find Danny Goldstein, by going quietly downstairs to page 93.

- You could wave to Simon and get him out of the service for a few minutes to tell you more about the mystery man, Abraham Samuels, if you haven't already done so, by going to page 86.

You ask Simon about Abraham Samuels

'It's funny you should ask about him again,' Simon begins, 'because Rachel and I used to find him mysterious when we were small. We used to imagine he was spy or a smuggler and things like that in our games until soon after my bar mitzvah. That's when I became a "son of the commandment", a religious adult, at the age of thirteen. I had to read from the Torah and make a short speech in synagogue. Afterwards I felt adult enough to ask Dad questions he'd avoided when I was smaller, and I asked him about Abraham Samuels. Dad told us Abraham's whole story. After that, we didn't play childish games about him any more.

'I'm not sure how much of the story you already know, so I'll start at the beginning. Abraham's parents were born round about 1900 in Germany. They were ordinary children, they were teenagers like us. They married. Then came the 1930s, and times gradually got worse for Jews there. Some left and went to live abroad. Some couldn't get exit visas because other countries wanted to limit the number of refugees coming in. Some didn't even try to leave, because they thought that things couldn't get any worse. Only they did get worse, far worse than anyone had ever imagined, in even their darkest nightmares.

'The Samuels' tried to live quietly, without drawing attention to their Jewishness. But of course even their name, plus observing Shabbat and going to synagogue, set them apart. Later they had by law to be registered as Jews and wear a yellow star. To us, any child of a Jewish mother is automatically a Jew. To the Nazis even someone with one Jewish grandparent was ounted as a Jew, whether the other three grandparents were Jewish or not.

'Papa Samuels – his first name was Jacob – was sacked from his job. People spat at him in the street. His wife got so frightened that she would not go out of the house. He had to do the shopping, at the few shops that would serve him. They had to start selling their valuable possessions to buy food. Their furniture and possessions gradually got less and less. The house looked emptier and emptier, as if a removal was going on.

'Every day, or rather every night, they were half-expecting that dreaded knock at the door. Did you know the SS nearly always came at night so that in the morning the neighbours would simply find an empty house? Any protests, any enquiries simply got you into trouble, for even the law was against our people. There was no-one you could turn to. No good going to the police, when the Nazi law said it was all legal. For some reason the Samuels parents were arrested in the daytime. They took both of them in broad daylight, but missed their little boy.

'Abraham was five. He was playing in the garden. At very great risk, the neighbours took him in and looked after him. Then, through an illegal Christian agency, they got papers and a woman smuggled him out of the country with her as her son. They came to England, where Abraham was adopted into a Jewish family. His adoptive parents are long dead, by the way, as you'd expect with so many years passing.

'Those two German neighbours also gave Abraham some vital information. You see, because his parents were arrested in the daytime, there were witnesses. The neighbours were watching from behind their net curtains and saw it all: the parents being taken into the street, pushed onto a lorry and driven away. They actually knew the officer who made the arrest. He was a young hothead who'd been caught into the Nazi party in its early days. I suppose it gave him a job, a uniform and status and power over people. The neighbours saw him shoving the Samuels' remaining valuable possessions into his pockets, including Jacob Samuels' expensive pocket watch. It had his initials engraved on it, and had been a twenty-first birthday present from his parents. Papa Samuels pleaded for it back, but the officer just laughed. But they saw him, you see, the people next door, and they knew him. That officer's name was Klaus Engelmann.'

You can't restrain a question: 'What happened to him, after the war?'

'Well,' Simon continues, 'Dad told me this was the big mystery. In the chaotic last days of the Third Reich all sorts of villains escaped from Germany and went abroad, even to the U.S.A. and the U.K., it's been said. One of the famous ones who was caught – kidnapped actually – and put on trial for war crimes was called Eichmann. But many more war criminals escaped than were caught. Lots of people now think it's too late to try to deal with them, but others think that genocide – the murder of a people – is such a terrible crime that it must never be allowed to be forgotten.

'Not surprisingly, when he grew up, Abraham became interested in Klaus Engelmann and where he'd gone. The names of those who carried out arrests or attacks were not often known, as their victims were mostly dead and there were usually no witnesses. Abraham, however, knew the name of the man who'd sent his parents to their death and robbed them of their property. So he got in touch with one of the Jewish groups dedicated to tracking down war criminals, Simon Wiesenthal's organization, and got them onto it.

'You'll never guess what they found out. It seems that Engelmann could see even by 1943 that Germany was probably going to lose the war – it was only a question of time. So he waited carefully and when the chance came he left the sinking ship, early in 1945. The investigators found out that Engelmann had not only escaped, but he too had come to the U.K. He'd done the double whammy! One day he had arrested a Jew who was carrying forged papers intended to get him out by a Jewish escape line, so Engelmann had used them himself. He had got himself smuggled out posing as this Jew. Engelmann had taken on a Jewish name and a Jewish identity.'

You interrupt again: 'But what about, err, circumcision? Aren't all Jewish males circumcised? Wouldn't Engelmann have been, err, noticed ...?'

Simon laughs. 'Brit Milah, the Covenant of Cutting, we call it. Yes, a good question and I'm not embarrassed by it. It's removal of the penis foreskin, performed on the eighth day after birth, with the emphasis on the covenant – the agreement with God – rather than the cutting! It's a Bible command from ancient times. But Muslims also do it, and some boys or men of any religion or none are circumcised for medical reasons. Engelmann was lucky. The tracking organization got hold of his medical record and found he'd been circumcised for medical reasons as a child, balanitis caused by phimosis, I suppose.'

Leaving aside the need for a medical dictionary to translate Simon's amazing biology knowledge, you ask, 'But didn't Engelmann drop his Jewish disguise when he got here?'

'The trail went cold from the point at which he left Germany. The name he took hasn't been uncovered yet. He might have changed it again when he arrived here. He might even have been trapped in his identity as a Jew.'

'What do you mean?'

'Well, he was smuggled out as a Jew, with Jewish papers, by Jews, and brought into the Jewish community here. If he'd dropped out he might have drawn attention to himself. Then he might have been arrested and tried for war crimes or received a rougher justice from the Jews he'd deceived. So it's even possible that he became a sort of prisoner of the very faith he had been trying to persecute. What if it captured him?'

'But the people who ran the escape line might have known the truth?'

'Not at the time, or they wouldn't have smuggled him out. Also, I don't think it's coincidence that soon after Engelmann reached England, the members of the escape line were betrayed and arrested. None survived the war.'

'Is there no clue to where he is now, this Engelmann?'

'Dad thinks he must be dead. If not, he'd be in his eighties. The Jewish agency never traced him any further, but we know that Abraham hasn't given up. After all, he's got a personal stake in this.'

You need time to think about this. It could be that you have hit on the beginning of the full solution of the mystery. Or it could be the end of a 'red herring', a clue that leads nowhere.

This is what you have. A non-Jew, previously responsible for arresting Jews and for stealing their money or valuables, poses as a Jew, escapes from wartime Germany and settles in England. He might have established another new identity but he might have been forced to retain his Jewish 'cover'. If he was obliged to continue with the Jewish cover, he might have had to attend synagogue and take part in the life of the Jewish community, at least on the surface, to escape detection or nosey questions. In fact, where

91

better to hide if you'd been persecuting Jews than right in the middle of them? It's the last place anyone would think to look. Very safe.

How does this fit in with what you are investigating? If Engelmann has survived, he must be in his eighties. None of the suspects or possible victims in this mystery is that old. But they are each young enough to be Engelmann's child ... Abraham, Danny, Miriam, David. But you know about the parents of some of them.

Are you on the verge of a solution?

While you think about this:

- If you have not yet been up to the landing outside the women's gallery to watch the synagogue service, walk quickly up the stairs to page 82.

- If you came here from the landing, search for Danny Goldstein by going to page 93.

- If you came here from recapping the main facts of the case, return to page 99.

- Otherwise, return to page 100 or page 101.

You search for Danny Goldstein

s you walk quietly down the corridor, you can hear
strange sound coming from the rabbi's office. It's a
nuffled noise, going on and on, as if someone is
alking, or rather, shouting with
hand – or gag – over their
nouth. You run into the
abbi's office. As you push
open the door you see
acing you, sitting in the
abbi's chair at the desk,
Danny Goldstein. His
hands are tied to the chair
rms and his feet to the
hair legs and he is gagged.
He's nodding in a terrified way at
 package on the rabbi's desk in front of him to draw
your attention to it. As you pause in the doorway to
ake the scene in, he stops his muffled cries for help.

In the silence you can hear a loud ticking like an
alarm clock. It is coming from the package on the desk:
 cardboard shoe-box sealed with sticky tape wrapped
ll round it. The writing on the wall spelt disaster for
Belshazzar. Amos with his fruit of summer, qayitz, saw
he end, qetz, of a people. Is this a bomb intended to
be the end of the synagogue and its people or the end
of Danny Goldstein?

Think quickly and choose:

Do you pick up the phone and dial 999 to get the police and the
bomb squad? To do this, go to page 95.

Do you pick up the package to take it out of the building before
it can explode? To do this, go to page 94.

Do you untie Danny to get him out of the room then evacuate
the building? To do this, go to page 96.

You pick up the package

Turn the page upside down to find out what happens next.

Very gingerly, you pick up the box. Danny's eyes seem to be out on stalks with fear as he watches you. Your hands are trembling slightly as you hold the box. Is the ticking louder, or is it your heartbeat – or just your imagination?

As you slowly move the box towards the edge of the rabbi's desk, ready to remove it from the room, the thing inside it slides along. You are horrified. If it's going to slide about like that, the package could explode in your hands. You decide that the best course of action would be to put it gently back down, release Danny and evacuate the building. So you carefully place the box in the waste-paper bin under the desk.

Turn the book the right way up and go to page 96 to untie Danny.

You decide to dial 999

You stride to the desk and pick up the phone, but there is a no dialling tone. You jiggle the button and dial 999 anyway. The number doesn't ring at the other end. The line must have been cut.

Quickly you must choose:

- Do you pick up the package to take it out of the building before it can explode, by going to page 94?

- Do you untie Danny to get him out of the room then evacuate the building, by going to page 96?

You untie Danny

You go across to Danny and start to untie him. Unfortunately it isn't as easy as it looks on the films. There the ropes and knots that hold people so securely seem to slide off in seconds when the hero comes to the rescue. You find yourself bungling around, and you forget in your hurry to take Danny's gag off first. After a few seconds you do remove it, so you can talk to him while you loosen the ropes. To your surprise he gasps,

'I'll admit it! I'll admit it! He can have the thing back if he wants! Anything, if only he'll leave me alone!'

But before you can ask Danny who the 'he' is and what 'the thing' is that he can have back, or what it is that Danny is so eager to admit, you see Abraham Samuels by the door, looking at you both. He is surprisingly calm.

'Quick!' you shout. 'There's a suspected bomb in here. You clear the people from the synagogue and contact the police while I untie Danny and get him out.' For a second or two, Abraham does nothing. He just stands and looks. Perhaps he's in shock. The three of you can hear the tick-tick-ticking. Abraham still doesn't move. Why hasn't he rushed off to clear the building? At last he speaks.

'I don't think you'll find that's a bomb,' he says. 'I think it's just a cheap bedroom alarm clock. Why don't you open the box and see?'

In these few seconds you might have seen the solution to the entire case. All the information you need to reach the solution has been revealed earlier in the book, if you can piece it together.

If you have worked out the right solution, you will know whether it is safe to open the cardboard box or not. But if you decide to open the box and it contains a bomb, it might explode. This

would immediately disqualify you from presenting any solution to the case.

- If you feel you need to recap quickly the main facts of this unusual case before you decide whether it is safe to open the box or not, go to page 99.

- If you want to risk opening the box, go to page 101.

- If you decide that the box should stay in the bin, unopened, until the bomb squad arrives, go to page 100.

One Final Clue

Turn the page upside down to read the clue then turn it back and follow the instructions at the bottom of the page.

Danny takes from his pocket a valuable old-fashioned pocket watch. He places it on the table as if to satisfy Abraham Samuels. Abraham Samuels picks it up and turns it over. Engraved on the back and quite clearly visible are the initials JS. Without another word, Abraham puts the watch into his pocket and walks out of the room.

You must now present your solution to the case. Remember, you need to work out:

• The intended victim

• The person responsible for the writing on the wall and the other happenings at the synagogue

• Their motive or reason for doing these things

Write down your solution then go to the mirror on page 102 to check it.

You recap the main facts of the case

If you missed the chance to talk to Simon about Abraham Samuels, read the conversation now by turning to page 86. Before you go to page 86, **bookmark this page** so that you can return to it afterwards. Then read on.

You try to list the facts and the questions in this very curious case:

FACTS

1. The first writing on the wall: 'Count, Count, Weigh, Divide'
2. The second writing on the wall: 'Summer'
3. The removal and defacing of the Goldstein parents' memorial
4. Four suspects – two can be safely eliminated
5. A probable intended victim – that leaves only one other suspect

QUESTIONS

1. What's the reason or motive? Revenge? Or getting the victim to own up to something?
2. How does the Engelmann/Samuels story fit in?
3. Is Danny's age significant?

• If you think you can now solve the case, write down your solution then go to the mirror on page 102 to check it. Remember, you need to get right:

  ▪ The intended victim
  ▪ The person responsible for the writing on the wall and the other happenings at the synagogue
  ▪ Their motive or reason for doing these things

• If you still can't make any sense of the case or work out all three parts of the solution, go to the final clue on page 98.

You decide the box should stay unopened

You must finish untying Danny then contact the police yourself, if Abraham Samuels won't help. You bend down to undo the last of Danny's knots. Before you can stop him, Abraham Samuels takes the box out of the waste-paper bin and rips off the sticky tape. Inside is an old-fashioned alarm clock, ticking loudly.

- If you think you can now solve the case, write down your solution then go to the mirror on page 102 to check it. Remember, you need to get right:
    - The intended victim
    - The person responsible for the writing on the wall and the other happenings at the synagogue
    - Their motive or reason for doing these things

- If you feel you need to recap quickly the main facts of this unusual case before you write down your solution, go to page 99.

- If you missed the chance to talk to Simon about Abraham Samuels, read the conversation now by turning to page 86. Before you go to page 86, **bookmark this page** so that you can return to it afterwards for another choice.

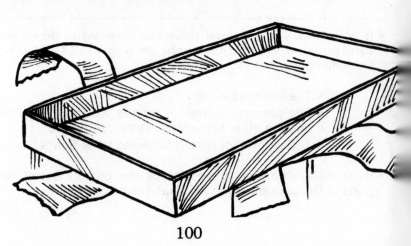

You risk opening the box

Inside it is an old-fashioned alarm clock, ticking loudly.

- If you think you can now solve the case, write down your solution then go to the mirror on page 102 to check it. Remember, you need to get right:
    - The intended victim
    - The person responsible for the writing on the wall and the other happenings at the synagogue
    - Their motive or reason for doing these things

- If you feel you need to recap quickly the main facts of this unusual case before you write down your solution, go to page 99.

- If you missed the chance to talk to Simon about Abraham Samuels, read the conversation now by turning to page 86. Before you go to page 86, **bookmark this page** so that you can return to it afterwards for another choice.

The Solution

The victim is Danny Goldstein. The writer on the wall, defacer of the memorial and inventor of the 'bomb' is Abraham Samuels. His motive was revenge. Getting back his father's watch can be counted as correct as an alternative.

Here are the details. Klaus Engelmann, the SS officer who had arrested the Samuels parents while Abraham, then a toddler, was playing in that garden, fled to England. He kept his Jewish disguise, both because it was hard to change identity again and because he thought it would be safer. He kept his assumed name of Goldstein and married a Jewish woman who knew nothing of his real past. They had one child, a son.

Engelmann-Goldstein died a year ago, just before Danny came to this synagogue looking for a job. Danny is Engelmann-Goldstein's son and 'caught' the same dislike of Judaism his father had. That's why he attended few services, didn't keep Shabbat, ate pork, etc. Remember?

Abraham Samuels had tracked Danny down and was trying to get him to admit his father's past, which Danny had discovered. Abraham also wanted the precious watch (JS engraving = Jacob Samuels), precious for its money value but much more for its memories as his parents' only surviving possession, the last link with them. Remember, as warden chairing the Management Committee he helped appoint Danny as security officer, so that he could watch him more carefully.

Abraham wanted to make Danny confess his father's identity and dark secret. He also wanted him to apologize for not making the facts public earlier and for not returning the watch and property stolen from other victims to their families. This led to his various threats in

102

writing and with the 'bomb'. If you tried to use the telephone when you found the 'bomb', remember how it was dead? It was never cut. You didn't check the wire. Abraham had simply unplugged it.

The attack on the memorial board stemmed from Abraham's desire to prevent the custom called (in Yiddish) Yahrzeit. This involves lighting a candle or, as in this case, switching on an electric light on the anniversary in the Jewish calendar of a loved one's death. Engelmann-Goldstein was a killer and a fraud. It seemed an insult to the Samuels parents and other war dead to commemorate him in a synagogue of all places. Abraham's own parents had no grave that could be visited and no death date that could be remembered by a visit to the grave or by switching on the light of memory. He deeply resented any attempt to remember Engelmann.

In the end, as you saw, Danny did admit the past and surrender the stolen watch, but perhaps both he and Abraham need help. You leave the rabbi to sort out what should happen to them next. Your work in uncovering what was going on is over.

Go to page 105 to work out your final score.

Working Out Your Final Score

You have spent 3 hours on Friday and 3 hours on Saturday working on the case **plus** the extra hours you chose to clock up or found you'd had to spend as the case went along.

First, calculate your total time score by adding 6 hours to the number of (extra) hours you have already noted down during the investigation.

Next, give yourself **1 penalty point** for each hour in your total time score.

Now add **3 penalty points** for each of the three parts of the solution you got **wrong**: the victim, the person who did the writing on the wall or their motive. Do not add anything for parts you got right.

Your final score is your total number of penalty points. The lower it is, the better. In fact the minimum score is 8 penalty points.

- If you scored 10 penalty points or less, go to page 107.
- If you scored 11 penalty points or more, go to page 106.

Time Score

~~1 hour~~ ~~2 hours~~ ~~3 hours~~ 3½ hours

$3\frac{1}{2} + 6 = 9\frac{1}{2}$ hours $= 9\frac{1}{2}$ penalty points

Solution

Victim, person who did writing right = no penalty points

Motive wrong = 3 penalty points

Final Score

$9\frac{1}{2} + 3 = \underline{\underline{12\frac{1}{2} \text{ penalty points}}}$

If you scored 11 penalty points or more

You go back to the Quicksolve office for a sandwich. A
you munch, you reflect that it has been a very unusua
case. You couldn't have been expected to grasp enoug
about the Jewish faith quickly enough to solve it. You
assistant collects together the books from the librar
and puts away the encyclopedias you've used in you
research. But as you put your feet on the desk and star
to relax with a coffee, the phone goes. Your assistan
answers then passes it to you saying:

'You must be getting well known for your work i
religious communities. Now we've got a Hindu templ
on the line with an urgent case to be investigatec
You'll have to get round there – better luck this time!'

THE END

If you scored 10 penalty points or less

Next day you go to dinner with the rabbi. The Levy family are all very welcoming and to your delight and surprise there is a massive meal, prepared after Shabbat, to celebrate the solution of the mystery. The watch has been returned to its proper owner. The rabbi is seeing the two central people later today. The affair is almost closed. All that remains is to tuck into a hearty meal and enjoy Jewish hospitality.

'But,' you wonder, 'I thought there were very strict food laws in your religion?'

'Oh, there are,' says David. 'For instance we don't use the same utensils for meat and milk dishes, nor do we mix them. We're lucky to have a double sink as we have to wash up the utensils separately too ...'

'I thought you just didn't eat pork.'

'It's more complicated than that. Pork just happens to be the well-known one. All vegetables and plants, all four-footed animals that chew the cud and have parted hoofs are OK – provided they're not diseased, killed by other animals, dead from old age, killed by an unsuitable method ...'

'That sounds incredibly complicated,' you agree.

'You get used to it when you've been brought up in the tradition, though.'

'Where did all these rules about food come from?'

'It's Torah and tradition. Some people say that in earliest Hebrew times, with no ways of refrigerating or preserving food, keeping a lot of the laws made sense as you avoided the foods that in a hot climate would most easily make you ill. That's not the point, though. What matters to us is that it is a way of obeying God, a way of giving a spiritual dimension to our eating habits. But it's not just *what* we eat. It's the meal itself. For instance, there's quite a long grace at the end of the meal, to thank God. The main bit of it is three paragraphs long!'

'Why at the end?'

'Because it's so long,' Rachel interrupts, laughing. 'The meal would go cold if we said it at the start.'

'In English it says: "Blessed are you, O Lord our God, King of the Universe. In your goodness you sustain the whole world. In grace, kindness and compassion He gives bread to all living beings, for His kindness extends throughout time and space ...'

'Dad,' interrupts Rachel again, 'we've not got there yet and our food's getting cold ...'

'Yes, do tuck in,' says Ruth. Your plate is heaped with food. It looks delicious. As you're about to begin, the phone rings in the entrance hall.

'Oh dear,' says Rabbi David, 'I hope I don't have to go out.' But Simon, who went off to answer the phone, comes back into the room and tells you it's for you. It's Quicksolve on the line. You groan as you get up and go to the phone. It's your assistant:

'Aren't you the lucky one? We've just had a phone call from a Hindu temple to say they've got a big problem and have heard that you've been successful and discreet in your previous work among other religious groups. They want you over there at once.'

It looks like you won't be able to eat your way through to the long grace after all. As far as this case and this meal go, it is:

THE END

Notes for Teachers

The Writing on the Wall can be used as a class library book in Key Stage 2 or to stretch able youngsters in this stage in RE. It can be used as part of the RE programme in Key Stage 3 or for lower-ability youngsters in Key Stage 4. It provides an opportunity to learn about Jewish artefacts, aspects of Jewish beliefs and worship, and an opportunity to develop skills in evaluating evidence. Readers have to distinguish probability and possibility in their interpretation of the clues. Cross-curricular skills – careful reading, analysis of data and decision-making – are all required throughout the text, and although there are choices and decisions for readers to make, the text is looped in such a way that all readers will read most of the text at some point in their progress through the book.

In particular The Writing on the Wall can be used:

- to introduce or revise work on synagogues or Jewish artefacts in a highly unusual way, perhaps before or after a class visit – in the text everyone explores the synagogue as part of the detective trail

- before interviewing a rabbi as part of a unit on Judaism in RE, so that the work of the interviewee can be compared with glimpses of Rabbi Levy in the story

- to introduce Judaism in an unexpected way in Key Stage 3, dissolving pupil expectations that they know it all already from primary-school Bible stories. Introducing Judaism via Abraham or Moses may produce a blasé response, but doing so via a mystery youngsters try to solve provokes thought

- to lead to an imaginative approach to studying places of worship and not merely a historical approach, providing an affective rather than a merely factual angle

- as an opportunity in Key Stage 3 for pairs or groups of youngsters to work together, negotiating paths to follow and discussing options as they progress through the case, and developing group-work skills in the process

- as a thriller for when the teacher is absent, to prevent classes from terrorizing the supply teacher or being bored into writing on the walls themselves!

- as an absorbing homework task which youngsters will want to finish to see 'whodunnit' – and in this case exactly what they 'dun'! Experience piloting the book suggests that youngsters will also go back after reaching the end to read the clues they've missed

- to introduce the Jewish Bible as a collection or book in its own right, not just as the 'Old' or somehow 'out of date' Testament
- above all to show that **RE can be fun!**

Using the genre of the mystery detective story, the reader is introduced to various concept and content areas in RE:

- important items in the synagogue (and their symbolism and/or function): Ark, bimah, menorah, Ner Tamid, Torah scroll and its dressings
- some items of religious dress: tallit, tefillin, yarmulkah
- synagogue personnel: hazzan (cantor), warden, rabbi, security officer
- various information about Jews and Jewish customs: bar mitzvah, circumcision, dietary rules, home and family, Judaism in the U.K., mezuzahs, the names of G-d, Orthodox/Reform differences, Shabbat, Yahrzeit candles
- some material about anti-Semitism and the impact of the Shoah or Holocaust
- the Jewish Bible: Hebrew and Aramaic languages, Books of Amos and Daniel, phrases that have come into the English language from it
- a number of religious and moral issues which classes might discuss, perhaps in small groups, after they have read the solution to the case: Do they feel the writer on the wall was right to do what they did? Do they have any sympathy for the victim? What would they advise the rabbi to do about all this? Do they think it is important to bring war criminals to justice, even 50 years on?

This book is **not** intended to replace systematic, careful study of Judaism or of synagogues or to provide a complete course on Jewish worship. While the writer has consciously tried to avoid stereotyping, youngsters may need to be cautioned to avoid making generalizations. Clearly not all Jews would think, talk or behave as the ones in this story do.

The book might be used in delivering RE or History or Art Attainment Targets and is intended to provide stimulus for a more thorough study of Judaism by supplying at least some 'plates' on which further experience and study can build. It also tries to develop affective responses in this area of religious study rather than leave students seeing Jewish Studies as irrelevant or abstract.

Although the text explains why many Jews prefer to see the printed form 'G-d', and do not pronounce the name, the form with vowel ('God') has been retained as standard so as not to confuse a mainly non-Jewish readership.